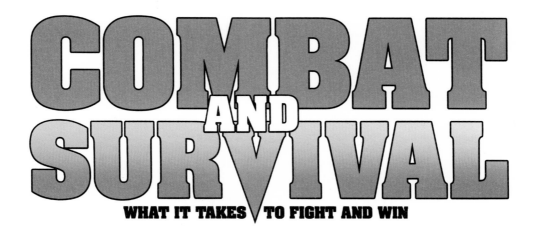

COMBAT AND SURVIVAL

WHAT IT TAKES TO FIGHT AND WIN

VOLUME
20

H. S. STUTTMAN INC. *Publishers*   Westport, Connecticut 06880

Contents

Volume 20

Published by H. S. STUTTMAN INC.
Westport, Connecticut 06889
© Aerospace Publishing 1991
ISBN 0-87475-560-3

4P(2295)20-90

FIGHTING THE ENEMY WITHIN

RUSSIAN SPECIAL FORCES TARGETS

Spetsnaz would be targeted against five different categories of target, listed in order of importance.

1. NUCLEAR DELIVERY MEANS
Other tasks would take a back seat until all land-based systems and their support had been disabled or destroyed.

2. HEADQUARTERS AND OTHER COMMAND AND CONTROL FACILITIES
All communication, signal and electronic warfare facilities would be attacked.

3. KEY AIRPORTS, ROADS AND RAIL SYSTEMS
In view of the quantity of military traffic, a small amount of sabotage could go a long way.

4. KEY INDUSTRIAL TARGETS
Massive damage could be inflicted by attacks on nuclear power stations, chemical plants, power lines and water supplies.

Note: All these acts would be likely to take place without any declaration of war.

In any future war the threat to mainland Britain is most unlikely to come in the form of large-scale invasion. The likelihood of the Soviets dispatching a vast fleet to land troops on the shores of Britain is so remote that it can be discounted. The main battle will be fought in North-West Europe and in particular in West Germany, where BAOR will be heavily involved.

But it will be vital for the Soviets to weaken and isolate Britain, as she will be an important base for reinforcing Europe with US and British troops, as well as being a vital NATO air and naval base. Mainland Britain, therefore, is likely to be subjected to missile and air attack, but she is also likely to be the target for sabotage raids aimed at vital installations and key points.

Enter the Spetsnaz

The Soviets have allocated specialist troops to attack these key points and vital targets behind NATO lines both on mainland Europe and in the UK. Known as Spetsnaz units, these are the special forces of the GRU, the Soviet Military Intelligence organisation. They are also sometimes known as ''diversionary brigades''. Their tasks in general war are the elimina-

A member of a Territorial Army UKLF battalion stands guard at one of Britain's many key points vital to her ability to wage a war in Europe against the Warsaw Pact. Soviet special forces will attempt to disrupt the battle in Europe by sabotage, ambush and assassination in the UK home base, from which the reinforcement of the British Army of the Rhine would be launched.

USAF security police

The United States Air Force has its own equivalent of the RAF Regiment and Provost Specialisation. You may well have to operate with them if your key point is one of the USAF air bases. They are well trained and equipped, but there are problems: you may be able to spot an imposter in your battalion, but how do you know the USAF policeman is what he appears to be?

Cruise carrier

The MAN 8×8 high-mobility tactical truck is currently used to transport cruise missiles from their bases to launch sites. It is not armoured, and provides little protection from small-arms fire. The escort formed in war by British Army units and the USAF Security Police is intended to combat any threat at a suitable distance from the carrier.

SPETSNAZ ATTACK

The primary aim of Russia's special purpose forces, the Spetsnaz, is to destroy NATO's nuclear delivery system before it can be effectively deployed. The Warsaw Pact has such massive conventional strength that it has no need to use nuclear weapons to achieve its goals in a war in Europe. These crack special forces teams could come in a variety of convincing guises, from civilian peace protesters to soldiers or police officers.

Agents

Both the GRU and KGB operate agents in the UK. Both are completely separate intelligence gathering networks. The GRU, the Soviet Military Intelligence Service, recruits its own agents and there may be little or no co-operation between them and the KGB. There are likely to be several hundred GRU agents operating in the UK.

Espionage

GRU agents are employed on 'strategic recce' tasks, i.e. they are looking for information on political systems, weak points in the economy that can be exploited to destabilise the government, and new military developments. They will also provide information of a lesser nature such as unit identities and deployments, troop movements etc.

Below: These forces will be indistinguishable from the rest of the population until they attack their targets. They will be exceptionally fit and will speak fluent English.

Above: Soviet special forces teams could arrive in the UK by any number of means, of which HALO (high-altitude low opening) would definitely be one. Many teams would be put in place well before the outbreak of war.

Air assets
Remember, unlike terrorists the Spetsnaz will be equipped with surface-to-air missiles capable of destroying your recce aircraft. They will usually not engage such targets until their primary key point target has been destroyed.

'Sleepers'
Agents can be active or sleeping. Active agents spy in peacetime, but sleepers spend their time becoming model citizens, building their cover and infiltrating groups that could be of use in war. The peace movement provides excellent cover for the detailed recce of nuclear key points. Others may have reached positions of authority in the government, army, police force etc. They will only become active when absolutely necessary in time of war.

Interrogation
A common Spetsnaz tactic is to take a prisoner and extract the maximum amount of information of immediate value before disposing of him, just prior to putting in an attack.

Joint operations
The police cannot be expected to deal alone with the threat posed by a Spetsnaz team, who are generally very highly trained and well equipped and could even be carrying chemical mines. Equally, the Army should not be required to deal with the public without police assistance.

Special purpose forces
In addition to agents, the GRU has its own special purpose forces, normally used for long-range recce and sabotage and operating in small groups, using GRU agents to provide support in the target country. The agents will provide accurate first-hand information on the group's operational area and the key points in it.

Stand-off attack
Spetsnaz will usually avoid a direct attack, preferring to destroy the target by means that allow them a good chance of getting away to destroy secondary targets and targets of opportunity.

Civilian police
You will have to work very closely with the civilian police in your area, as only they will have the background information necessary to enable you to have any chance of sorting out the enemy from the civilians.

tion of enemy political and military leaders and attacks on enemy nuclear delivery systems, communication centres and military HQs in the field. They might also attack civilian targets such as power stations, storage depots and other government installations.

Largest special forces

Spetsnaz forces number between 27,000 and 30,000 men in the Soviet Army and Navy, making them by far the largest special forces group in the world. They are equipped with the 5.45-mm AKS-74 assault rifle, silenced pistols and hand grenades. A Spetsnaz group will also carry a SAM-7 anti-aircraft missile launcher and mines and explosives for demolition purposes. You can recognise them easily because they wear the uniform of the airborne and air assault forces or, if they are naval special forces, of the naval infantry.

It is not known precisely how many Spetsnaz are targeted against the UK, but you can assume that they will be infiltrated into the country by submarine, High Altitude Low Opening (HALO) parachute insertion techniques — or they may simply arrive by scheduled air or sea passenger services during a period of tension. They could be disguised as tourists, sports teams, cultural groups, businessmen or members of diplomatic missions. Entry into the UK would almost certainly be by way of a third country.

Such infiltrators would obviously

Combat Skills

Until war is declared the army can only act in support of the police, and every military act is still subject to the normal criminal law. This sniper rifle is connected to a Polaroid camera to give the firer's view of the target at the moment of firing.

wear civilian clothes and would contact sleeper agents as guides and sources of information, shelter and transport. Naval Spetsnaz units would infiltrate mainly by sea, using submarines to approach close to their targets and then reach the shore by midget submarine, inflatable or by swimming.

Lower standards

While Spetsnaz troops are known to be professional and well-trained, it is unlikely that they measure up to our own SAS troops. Selection methods are not so demanding, they are not so comprehensively trained, and they do not have the same degree of operational experience. It is true that they have operated against rebel tribesmen in Afghanistan, although they have not found this at all easy.

They are really better compared with our own Marines or Parachute Regiment, who are also taught to operate in small groups. While Spetsnaz expertise should not be underestimated, the indications are that it would be possible to thwart their operations and defeat them in battle.

You are just as likely to be looking for Spetsnaz in mainland UK as fight-

ing a more conventional battle in BAOR. In the event of war a large part of the British Army stays this side of the Channel to defend the home base. And it is by no means a second-class role. Home defence is considered just as important as the job of BAOR. Home defence forces consist of Regular infantry battalions, Territorial Army (TA) battalions and the Home Service Force (HSF).

The TA is recruited on a county or regional basis and is particularly well suited to defending the area in which most of its members live. The HSF started in 1982. The aim is to expand it

to a force of 47 companies by 1990 (or a total force of 4,500 men). It is part of the TA and its role is to defend vital installations. The TA and the HSF will be used mostly on static tasks guarding key points and vulnerable installations.

This will release the Regular infantry units to act as quick reaction forces and mobile reserves to react to any problem throughout the country. This could be to reinforce a key point that is under attack, or to search for and destroy a Spetsnaz unit that may have been located in a particular area.

Something different

You will be lightly armed and equipped in a Home Defence battalion. You will be transported in "soft skinned" trucks and Land Rovers, since the vast majority of armoured vehicles will have gone to reinforce BAOR. If you are extremely lucky there may be a few RAF Chinook or Puma helicopters remaining in the

Nuclear delivery means are the primary target for Spetsnaz attack. Dispersion on mobile launchers reduces their vulnerability to attack. But 'Cruise watching' by peace groups has certainly undermined the value of mobile-launched cruise missiles.

Many regular battalions assigned to home defence have a wealth of experience in internal security operations in Northern Ireland, which would prove very useful.

The helicopter snap VCP seen here in the border country of South Armagh would have equal application in dominating a patrol area around a key point.

UK. This is the ideal form of transport for any quick reaction force.

Home defence battalions have a minimal scaling of MILAN and other infantry support weapons. You are unlikely to need them in the sort of purely infantry operations in which you are likely to be involved in the UK. Surveillance devices are, on the other hand, particularly important when you are guarding something. You will therefore want to ensure that you get hold of any night vision equipment that is available if you are given the task of guarding a key point.

Home defence involves a whole lot of people you will not have come across before. Quite apart from the TA and the HSF (and you could equally well work with the TA in BAOR), the Royal Navy is responsible for guarding many of its dockyards though, because the vast majority of its sailors are at sea, you may be called upon to guard naval facilities as well. Regular sailors are supported by the Royal Naval Reserve (RNR) and the Royal Naval Auxiliary Service (RNXS).

The Royal Air Force is reinforced by the Royal Auxiliary Air Force. It and RAF Regiment Regulars are responsible for guarding airfields. You will also come across Army Reservists, some of whom are formed into General Support Units. And you may work with US troops who will be defending US bases.

Within the law

Lastly and, most important of all, you will be working with the civilian police. All operations on the UK mainland are subject to the normal working of the law. There will almost always be policemen operating with military units, and the army operates in support of the police. So you can see that if, in some respects, home defence is not so glamorous as soldiering in

BAOR, the task is certainly very different and very challenging. It is much less straightforward, and you need to be aware of what you can do, when you can do it, and where you can do it. You will need to know something about organisations with whom you would not normally work.

If vital air bases, naval dockyard facilities, ammunition dumps, radio

Quick-reaction force Land Rovers fitted with GPMGs fire their weapons as part of a live-firing exercise on Salisbury Plain. The majority of UKLF battalions will be carried in Land Rovers rather than APCs.

Spetsnaz will also aim to cause maximum disruption to road, rail and air communications to prevent their effective use for the deployment of the huge quantities of men and matériel, British and American, required in Germany.

or radar installations or indeed any one of a host of other installations are damaged or destroyed, it could well affect our soldiers fighting in Europe. That is why home defence is so important.

Basic soldiering

In many ways, home defence will involve you in the basics of infantry soldiering. You will operate mostly on your feet, with a pack on your back. The heaviest weapon you are likely to use will be your rifle or the section's LSWs. You will need to be up to date with your basic infantry skills of patrolling, movement at night, surveillance, carrying out search-and-destroy missions in woodland, digging a fire trench and much more besides. It could not be more different to working in a Warrior battalion in BAOR. Arguably, home defence soldiering is closer to "real" infantry work.

Helicopter support will usually be provided by the few Pumas and Chinooks that do not go to Germany. Some Wessexes may be available from Northern Ireland.

Spetsnaz will be difficult to distinguish from the rest of the community. They may well be aided by 'sleepers' who occupy important positions in the security forces.

Combat Report
Malaya:
Terrorist Engagement Part 1

Richard Williams served in the British Army during the Malayan Emergency. This is the story of an encounter with terrorists in 1953.

We were deep in the Pahang jungles of central Malaya. The Whirlwind helicopter rose at full power from the clearing until it had cleared the top of the surrounding trees. It dipped its nose forward and, with a cheery wave from the crewman at the open door, rapidly disappeared from view.

Covered by Jones with his Bren gun, I moved towards the hut at the edge of the clearing. It had been attacked and destroyed by our regiment a month earlier. The two communist terrorist occupants had been killed, but I wasn't taking any chances. I carefully searched the hut, fireplace and water hole for signs of recent occupation. There were none, so Jones got a brew going while we waited for the helicopter to return.

We were getting warm!

We had a long wait ahead of us. The helicopter had to make a 40-minute round trip to bring in two 15-man platoons for our operation. It would be noon before we moved out. I suddenly thought of the consequences if the chopper failed to return: it would take four days' march to get back to the road. I didn't fancy that, so while Jones was making the tea I set up the radio and contacted our second-in-command, who was supervising the helicopter's movements.

Our task was to locate another clearing that was reportedly occupied by an unknown number of terrorists. It was two days' march away, across a 2,000-ft mountain range. The helicopter had kept low bringing us in, so there was little chance of the enemy knowing of our presence. All had gone according to plan, and at one o'clock we moved off towards our objective.

By noon on the second day we were following a ridge track, about a thousand metres

The Platoon got sorted out in the helicopter LZ hacked out of the jungle. The terrorist camp was surrounded by massive tree trunks like these.

short of the reported position. Suddenly my leading scout stopped and pointed to a fresh scrape of mud among the moist leaves. A boot had slipped as the wearer climbed a steep slope. The footprint bore the unmistakable markings of the basketball boot favoured by the terrorists. We were getting warm!

I motioned both platoons off the track, posted sentries and got together a five-man recce patrol. We dropped our packs and moved forward. Moving slightly to the left of the track, we slowly advanced about five hundred metres. Suddenly I smelt the whiff of Chinese cigarettes. I raised my hand to halt the patrol and signalled to them to get down in the undergrowth.

We had been hiding for about 10 minutes when suddenly, off to the left, came the sound of chopping wood. After months of fruitless patrolling we were finally going to see some action.

I swapped places with my leading scout and brought my second Bren gunner, the deadly Edwards, up to cover me. I moved forward by short leaps, pausing after every bound to look and listen. The chopping grew louder, and we began to catch faint snatches of Chinese. Then I saw a break in the trees. Slipping silently from tree to tree, I slowly advanced towards the clearing. It took half an hour. I picked a sprig of leaves from a nearby bush and crept the last few paces, ending up behind a big tree right on the edge of the clearing.

I raised the leaves in front of my face, and peered round the tree. At that moment I suddenly realised that my M2 carbine was resting in the crook of my right arm as if I was going for a day's gentle rough shooting. For a split second I thought of moving back to the tree and changing my hold, but I instantly dismissed that idea. Movement was probably more dangerous than not having my gun ready. Besides, I had shot plenty of rabbits from that position, and they didn't give you much time to aim and fire.

I counted the terrorists

The track we'd been following led straight to a hut about 50 metres from me. The hut was open-sided. I counted five terrorists: three in the hut and two around a fire nearby. As I watched, a sixth appeared from the right. He was carrying two large tins suspended from a pole over his shoulder. As he walked, water splashed from one of them. Clearly, the water hole was to the right of the camp. I would have to make sure we covered it when we made our assault.

They were obviously about to start preparing their evening meal. I glanced at my watch: it was already four o'clock! We had to get a move on or there was a danger of not completing the attack before darkness, at around six-thirty. I slid back behind the tree and, taking care to keep it between me and the hut, silently rejoined my patrol.

I gave details of what I'd found, then told them to be ready in half an hour. My orders were for a five-man assault team, including Edwards, to cover the path, under my command. As soon as we were in position the remainder of the force, under Peter, the commander of the other platoon, were to surround the clearing. They were to spread out and keep back, without losing sight of each other or the clearing, and were to remain there until they heard the first shot. Then they were to run forward and take up kneeling fire-positions behind trees on the edge of the clearing, and shoot any terrorist who came towards them.

Flying in and out of the tiny landing zones was no easy business. Here an RAF Whirlwind heads for home after dropping off an infantry patrol.

Machine-guns were to cover the edge of the clearing, although their range of fire was poor as the whole area was criss-crossed by fallen trees. At least this meant that anyone attempting to cross the clearing in a hurry would be an easy target.

Peter and a light machine-gunner were to cover the track down to the water hole. His sergeant was to lead the rest of the encircling force to link up with my assault party, then the attack would begin. If anything went wrong, we would assault at once.

It was time to move off

The two signallers and the dog handler with his dog were to guard the pack. They were to set up the antenna and establish communications with base as soon as they heard the first shot.

I didn't want a single sound while we moved into position, so I made every man jump up and down to see if anything rattled. Then I double-checked that rounds had been correctly loaded.

Finally, it was time to move off. I was soon in position with my assault party and watching the rest of the force move off to surround the clearing. I knew Peter would move slowly and carefully to make sure we took them by surprise. It would take at least an hour for them to move round. When the last man had disappeared, I told the party to sit and keep a careful watch while Edwards and I covered the track. There were occasional snatches of sound.

Another 10 minutes went by . . . then suddenly there was a shot to my left. Damn! Quickly leaping to my feet, I ordered the others to charge and set off down the track towards the camp. Some idiot had obviously left the safety catch off his rifle. I would make sure that whoever it was got 28 days' detention.

This all took place before the Vietnam era of mass helicopter assaults. The platoon was ferried in to the LZ in two trips by a single Whirlwind.

DEFENDING KEY POINTS

The only effective way to deter a Spetsnaz patrol from getting close is to play them at their own game and hunt them out with some aggressive patrolling and ambushing. Most attacks will come at night, where sophisticated night vision devices will be essential.

In the event of war, the United Kingdom would be divided into Home Defence Regions. In each region, a joint service headquarters would be established that would command all military manpower and the resources allocated to them. These regions would be further sub-divided into military tactical areas of responsibility (TAORs). These TAORs would normally have a common boundary with either police force or county boundaries to make liaison with the civil police and local authorities easier. They also provide a framework within which Home Defence forces can be deployed.

The job of the Regular Army, the Territorial Army (TA) and the Home Service Force (HSF) in war in the United Kingdom is clearly the defence of the British Isles. As we have already

This US serviceman, equipped with an M16A2 with M203 underbarrel grenade-launcher, stands guard with full NBC protection on a key point defence exercise on one of the US bases in the UK. Outside the perimeter the British Army, both regular and Territorial, await the enemy in the form of the Special Air Service, who will use Russian special forces tactics to attack the base.

Overt guards are of limited use against the Spetsnaz attack. Covert OPs have far more chance of collecting information and surviving long enough to pass news of the attack onto the Quick Reaction Force. The NOD image intensifier usually used by the artillery in conventional operations is ideal for this task.

seen, this is unlikely to involve you in operations against a large-scale invasion. The threat is from specialist enemy troops who have been inserted into the UK covertly and who will attempt to destroy vital NATO, British and US installations.

It is one of the Army's main tasks to provide guards for static vulnerable installations, or 'key points' (KPs). You could be guarding anything, from a British Telecom communications tower to a military headquarters to a naval port facility.

Key values

Guarding KPs is the 'bread and butter' of home defence. A KP is defined as an establishment whose disruption or destruction will result in damage to the national war effort. KPs are categorised according to their importance. Their value is also limited by time and space: for instance, a communications KP might be important only until some particular information has been passed through it. And if the KP you are

Naval Spetsnaz
The Naval Special Purpose forces are Russia's largest special forces unit. Each of the four fleets has its own Spetsnaz brigade. They have a similar function to Britain's Special Boat Section but are not trained to the same standard. Many of the tasks carried out by the Royal Marines would normally be undertaken by naval Spetsnaz.

Submarine-launched attack
An attack could be launched from a conventionally-powered 'Kilo'-class submarine equipped with a lock-out hatch to deploy divers in a submersible delivery vehicle. The submarine could deploy the SDV as far out as 18km from the target, carrying blister charges large enough to destroy a rig by cutting the legs at depth.

KEY TARGETS

Russian Special Forces will not limit themselves to purely military targets; key economic targets would also be attacked. In Britain, this would mean that oil industry installations both on- and offshore would be targeted: if these installations were destroyed it would seriously undermine Britain's ability to fight a conventional war. Defending the North Sea rigs is the job of the Royal Marine Commandos.

Royal Marines
In war, the Royal Marines would be deployed to northern Norway and only a limited presence would be available to guard the North Sea rigs. Defence would rely on a quick reaction force deployed by helicopter after warning of attack or when the attack was under way.

guarding is a cruise missile convoy, then the ground it occupies is significant only while the convoy remains there.

KPs also vary in size – from very large complex areas, such as a port, an airfield, or communication 'aerial farm' of many acres, to covert equipment in ordinary buildings – such as a computer controlling some vital function – and underground hardened complexes with small concealed entrances.

Within each KP will be a number of vulnerable points (VPs) upon which the function of the KP is dependent. These will often include the KP's power generators and associated fuel supplies, including the fuel runs between them. Many KPs will have 'tail-outs', parts of VPs that run outside the perimeter fence for considerable distances before the dispersal of its vital function, or other factors, make it no longer a VP. Examples are a communications line running underground from a KP until it disperses into the

British Telecom system, or a single-track railway line running from an ammunition depot until it joins the main railway system.

Four threats

Although you must take into account the threat from conventional bombing when you are planning the defence of a KP, you should devote most of your resources to countering the land threat. This will probably take place in one of four different ways:

1 A covert attack: an attempt by sabotage to penetrate the perimeter, sabotage the vital part of the installation (probably with explosives) and withdraw without being discovered.
2 An overt armed attack: an attack by a formed body of enemy to overpower the guard and destroy the function of the KP.
3 A stand-off attack: the use of stand-off weapons such as a rocket launcher or anti-tank guided weapon.

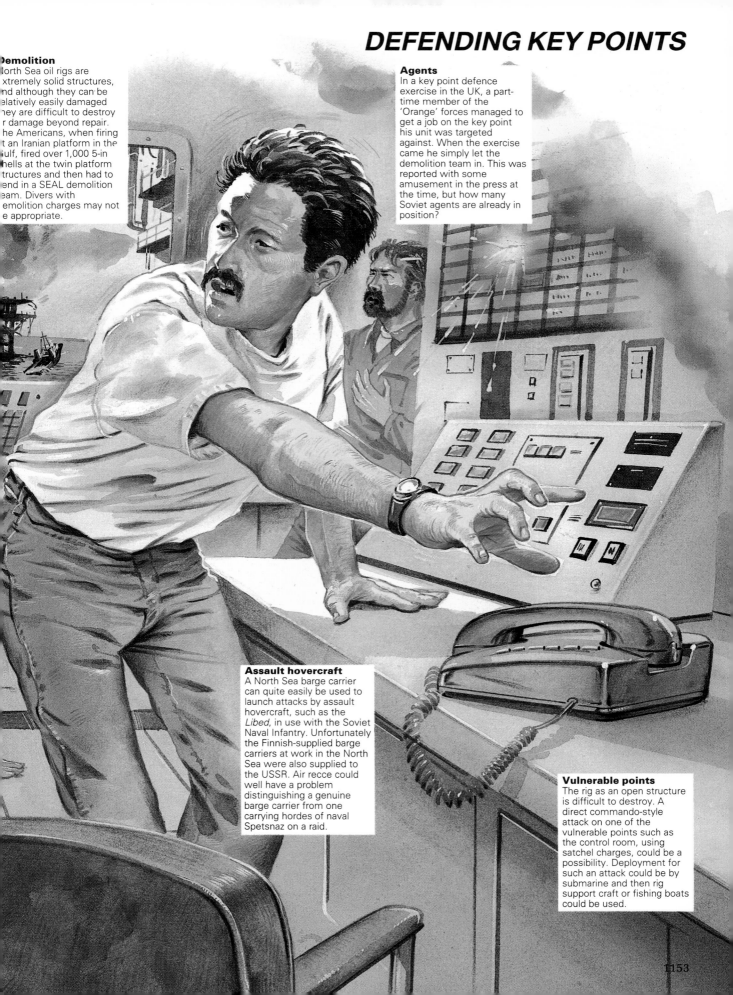

Demolition

North Sea oil rigs are extremely solid structures, and although they can be relatively easily damaged they are difficult to destroy or damage beyond repair. The Americans, when firing at an Iranian platform in the Gulf, fired over 1,000 5-in shells at the twin platform structures and then had to send in a SEAL demolition team. Divers with demolition charges may not be appropriate.

Agents

In a key point defence exercise in the UK, a part-time member of the 'Orange' forces managed to get a job on the key point his unit was targeted against. When the exercise came he simply let the demolition team in. This was reported with some amusement in the press at the time, but how many Soviet agents are already in position?

Assault hovercraft

A North Sea barge carrier can quite easily be used to launch attacks by assault hovercraft, such as the *Libed*, in use with the Soviet Naval Infantry. Unfortunately the Finnish-supplied barge carriers at work in the North Sea were also supplied to the USSR. Air recce could well have a problem distinguishing a genuine barge carrier from one carrying hordes of naval Spetsnaz on a raid.

Vulnerable points

The rig as an open structure is difficult to destroy. A direct commando-style attack on one of the vulnerable points such as the control room, using satchel charges, could be a possibility. Deployment for such an attack could be by submarine and then rig support craft or fishing boats could be used.

You should set up an operations room on your KP to co-ordinate the activity of the Army, the police and any other organisations involved in guarding it. The ops room should be as invulnerable as possible and all communications should be duplicated.

4. Laser target marking: the 'marking' of a KP for a stand-off or air-delivered weapon by a laser target marker.

A static guard is always at a disadvantage. The enemy have the advantage of surprise and of being able to concentrate their forces undetected at a point of their own choosing. So a small detachment guarding, for instance, a radio rebroadcast station could find itself under attack by a highly professional Spetsnaz unit armed with automatic weapons, demolition equipment and possibly stand-off weapons such as an RPG-7 rocket launcher or even a laser target marker (LTM) to guide laser guided munitions (LGM) dropped from an aircraft onto a KP. The level of threat from a Spetsnaz unit may not always be so severe, but in some cases it may be and in these circumstances you would want reinforcing quickly by a Quick Reaction Force (QRF).

Do what you can

Invariably you will be short of men and materials to defend a KP. Since we do not have National Service in this country, there are no vast reserves of manpower; consequently there are too few soldiers to guard a great many KPs. All your assets, therefore, must be devoted entirely to achieving your aim, which is to safeguard the function of the KP. Don't dissipate your energy on other tasks, however important they may seem. For instance, you may not be able to follow up a fleeing enemy, however desirable this may seem in itself.

A large KP complex might be guarded by a platoon of 30 men with perhaps a section on sentry duty inside or on the perimeter, a section on patrol outside the KP trying to prevent a stand-off attack, and a third section resting and acting as a reserve and local QRF.

Close defence

The section responsible for the close defence of a KP would be responsible for the close guarding, probably with a two-man guard, of any VPs within the perimeter. Certainly one man would be on the gate controlling the access of vehicles and pedestrians. A 'prowler guard' of two men might

patrol the perimeter fence, and another single sentry might man an OP on a high point within the perimeter.

You would need to dig trenches, which the close-defence section could man in the event of a concerted attack, particularly an air attack. You would need to sandbag any vulnerable equipment such as computers or generators, or you could screen it off with hessian, thus denying an enemy stand-off weapon an aiming mark.

You could thicken up the perimeter fence with concertina wire, and you could install an infra-red 'fence' or unattended ground sensor (UGS) system if either were available. It may well be that some perimeter protection equipment such as closed-circuit TV is already in place. In that case, you would co-locate your control centre with the TV monitors.

Outside the KP

The section dominating the ground around the KP could mount any combination of overt vehicle or foot

Royal Electrical and Mechanical Engineers construct a sanger on a corner of a KP perimeter fence. You need several layers of sandbags for overhead protection: you could be mortared or rocketed in addition to air attack.

Spetsnaz will be trained to a standard far beyond that which we could hope to achieve among the defending forces, and their equipment, such as this unattended remote radio jammer, will be the equal of ours.

patrols with covert standing patrols or observation posts (OPs) appropriate to the particular location. To do this effectively, put yourself in the mind of the enemy and try to work out how he would attack the KP.

You will have to dominate stand-off attack positions and approach routes to the KP. This would require an intelligent appreciation of the situation by you, a good eye for ground, clever planning and good fieldcraft. You must remain one step ahead of the enemy if you are going to stand any chance of heading off his attack.

If you are in a populated area, you can tell the locals to keep their wits about them and to report by telephone any suspicious movement or individuals they may notice. These extra pairs of eyes will be invaluable and an advantage that the enemy will not enjoy. He may have initiative but, if you prepare your position properly, put yourself in the mind of the enemy and remain alert, you should be able to frustrate his attack on KPs. It is an important job; you will be defending your own country or perhaps even your county or town. What could be more important?

Above: Unmanned ground sensors such as 'Classic' can be deployed to cover all the likely approach routes to a KP several kilometres out, and can be set to warn of vehicle and/or infantry approach.

Below: A Tomahawk cruise missile in flight. The Russian equivalent could be launched from a Tu-26 'Backfire' up to 1,200 km from a target and then precision-guided using laser target marking.

Above: This is the effect of a Tomahawk cruise missile, conventionally armed with a 1,000-lb warhead, on a concrete block house. Laser target marking would also be used for toss bomb attacks.

Right: Hardened aircraft shelters provide a fair degree of protection from conventional bombing: only a direct hit will be effective. Laser target marking by Russian Special Forces and the new generation of smart munitions virtually guarantees direct hits.

Combat Report
Malaya:
Terrorist Engagement Part 2

Modelling a captured Communist terrorist cap. Catching the enemy in their camp often provided valuable intelligence as well as prized trophies.

Richard Williams continues his story of an engagement in the Malayan jungle in 1953.

As I ran I flicked my safety catch off, which was just as well, for just as I reached the clearing three terrorists were trying to escape. They had their packs on, weapons at the ready, and were coming straight towards me. They were so intent on getting away that I saw the leading one a fraction of a second before he saw me. I stopped and aimed my carbine. At that moment he saw me, and let off a round from the hip. It was the last thing he ever did, for as he started to re-cock his rifle I shot him through the head with my first round.

I swung my aim on to the second terrorist, who was turning to run in the opposite direction. Two, three, four, five rounds gone, all carefully aimed at his back, at only 15 yards. Why didn't he fall? After the fifth round he was still running. I couldn't tell if he had dived or fallen, but he went down into a natural fold in the ground and rolled over, so I could just see the top of his head.

I became aware of firing from the rest of the assault party and, glancing round, saw that they had taken up positions on the edge of the clearing. They were directing their fire at the hut, where I saw two more terrorists picking up their packs and making off towards the track leading to the water hole. The third member of the party we had bumped into had run behind a tree near the hut, and was firing back at us.

"Charge!"

I decided to concentrate on the two making for the water hole. They were 50 yards away, and had only about 25 yards to go before they would be out of sight and danger. I dropped to one knee and fired a rapid succession of shots. Twenty-two rounds of .30 ammunition to a magazine; only seven rounds left before I would have to change it. We had to get after them quickly, or they would get clean away. Jumping to my feet, I shouted "Charge!" and "Fire at the man behind the tree!"

I fired from the shoulder position as I went towards the tree. The others did the same. Surely we must have got him? At that moment, about five yards to my right, I saw a muzzle flash. To this day I can still see it. It seemed to hang there for ages. Missed! Good! Get him! Raise your rifle! First pressure! Aim between

8 Platoon with a fine array of hardware, including No. 5 jungle carbine, No. 4 rifle, a Bren gun, US M2 carbine and Marlin UD M42 sub-machine gun.

the eyes! Fire! There was a click, but nothing happened.

Blast Jones! I had given him my carbine and magazines to check and clean while I was giving out orders. Why didn't he tell me there were only 17 rounds in it?

The terrorist started to re-cock his rifle. I stepped back, out of his view, to change magazines. Press the release catch, drop the empty magazine, open pop-stud on magazine pouch, struggle for a second or two to get the new magazine out and re-cock the weapon. As I did so a round flew out of the chamber. Hell, was it only a misfire? I glanced at the discarded magazine. Sure enough, there were rounds there. Idiot, why didn't you stick to the immediate action drill? Steady, boy, don't panic. Get a grip and get on with it.

I fired and hit him

"Give me covering fire," I shouted to Edwards. He immediately let loose five rapid shots, which threw up the earth in front of the terrorist. While Edwards fired I ran forward until my target was in view. I raised my carbine. The terrorist was five yards away from me. The muzzle of his rifle was on the ground as Edwards unleashed another barrage of shots. As I looked through my sights, I saw brown eyes looking back at me as though they knew exactly what was going to happen. Why didn't he fire at me? I fired, and hit him straight between the eyes. His head dropped instantly.

I looked up to see the last remaining terrorist disappearing into the jungle. Although we all shot at him, he got clean away.

Telling the others to follow, I dashed across to the water hole. On the far side of the stream there were footprints leading diagonally up the bank. I followed the trail for 400 yards until it hit a ridge line, where there was a forester's track, and it petered out. I cast along for about two hundred yards in each direction, but it was impossible to see anything. Besides, it would soon be dark and I wanted to get back to the clearing to find out what had happened to the rest of the force.

We deliberately made a lot of noise and called out to announce our presence as we re-approached the clearing. I knew the men would be jumpy and I didn't want to be another "own goal" statistic.

The light was fading fast by the time we reached the clearing. I could see that Peter had already collected the signaller, dog-handler and packs, and had set the men to work making a base for the night.

"Any casualties?" I asked Peter.

"Sergeant Walker is wounded," he replied. He was my platoon sergeant.

"What on earth happened?" I asked. By an extraordinary piece of bad luck, just as he had got round a corner of the clearing Peter had spotted a terrorist wearing a pack and carrying a rifle, coming towards them. There was nothing they could do except sink down and watch him come closer and closer. When he was almost on top of them they had no option but to shoot him. That was the shot I had heard.

Speared by a pig trap

Following the standard drill they had then charged into the clearing towards the hut. My platoon sergeant had had the misfortune to run into a trap that had been set to catch pigs raiding crops. He had been speared right through the thigh by a nine-inch piece of sharpened bamboo.

I was pleased to discover that during the half hour I had been trying to follow the escaped terrorists my medic had pulled the spear out, cleaned and bandaged the wound and administered a shot of morphia to relieve the pain.

I also discovered why the terrorist behind the mound hadn't fired. Apparently one of Edwards's rounds had sheared the bolt of his rifle off, so he couldn't cock it.

The helicopter came at midday for my sergeant. He had to share the back with three dead terrorists. The rest of us were back at the road two days later.

Reconnaissance by fire with an M2 carbine. A handy little weapon whose only fault was the low stopping power of its .30 'short rifle' cartridge.

SEARCH AND DESTROY

Most Home Defence Forces are likely to be tied up in guarding static installations — but you won't eliminate the enemy threat if you spend all your time on the defence. Home Defence forces must be able to provide formed bodies of troops to act as reserves, so that they can undertake operations anywhere in their area of responsibility. The two forms of mobile operation that you are most likely to undertake are Search and Destroy or Cordon and Search.

A mobile patrol of the Royal Irish Rangers on Home Defence duties. The stripped down and heavily-armed Land Rover provides the teeth of the Quick Reaction Force.

Exercise 'Orange' forces photograph a railway bridge to provide the information on which a night patrol and close target recce on the bridge will be based. The team will usually lay up within striking distance of the target during daylight. It is the job of the Home Defence battalions to search and then destroy.

Police responsibilities
The police usually decide on the area to be searched, and then carry out a plain-clothes recce of the target. During the operation they will provide Special Branch officers to evaluate any intelligence gathered on the spot. They will also carry out the search and screening and be in charge of warning the local population that the search is taking place once the cordon is in position.

Search parties
Search parties would be made up of police officers with an escort of troops. They are responsible for the complete search of the buildings and inhabitants. The search party may include specialists such as Explosive Ordnance Disposal (EOD) Officers.

Reserve
You must maintain a reserve or reaction force to be deployed in case of trouble. A Spetsnaz group have the ability to do damage out of all proportion to their size.

Fields of fire
In a residential area your fields of fire are going to be restricted. You must position troops so that the arcs of fire are sufficient to allow them to identify the target and fire into relatively safe killing zones: this will not be easy.

Curfew
As soon as the cordon is in place the local inhabitants should be warned that a curfew is in force. This should be enforced by the police. Most searches are carried out in the very early hours of the morning, so control of movement should not be too much of a problem.

Screening cage troops
These troops set up the prisoner cages and guard those people prior to interrogation.

Cordon and search operations

The aim of cordon and search operations is to kill or capture wanted people, Russian special forces agents, assassins and sabotage teams and their supporters, and to capture their equipment preferably before it can be used. You must remove very dangerous and fanatical enemy from the midst of a civilian community without using the firepower or techniques that you would normally employ when taking out an enemy position.

Search and destroy operations, as their name implies, probably involve at least a company-sized unit searching a large area of countryside for an elusive and small enemy force such as a Spetsnaz unit, locating it, pinning it down and destroying it. In conventional warfare the destruction of the enemy may be achieved by air power or artillery, but this would not be the case in home defence operations (mainly because the aircraft and guns are not available – they will virtually all be deployed in Germany and elsewhere) but also because such operations would be inappropriate in the UK, so infantry companies would have to locate and destroy such targets using infantry weapons. However, helicopters and RAF training aircraft such as the Beagle, which it is planned to form into Regional Air Squadrons, would be an invaluable surveillance aid in a search and destroy operation.

The first report of enemy troops in a particular location may have come from a sighting from the air or, more likely, from an alert and suspicious member of the civil population. Aircraft might be used to verify a sighting and, in the unlikely event that they are available, helicopters could be used to achieve surprise by flying in troops.

Company operations

In a company-sized operation, one platoon might be dropped as a 'stop line' beyond the enemy location and the two other platoons could be

Escort troops
You will need a small force to escort suspects to and from cages and to places of detention, e.g. police cells. Remember that some of these suspects may be Spetsnaz and therefore very dangerous even when unarmed.

In cordon and search operations you will have the problem of sorting the enemy from the civilians, some of which are going to be less than co-operative. Remember, handle with caution: Spetsnaz are very highly trained in unarmed combat.

Inner cordon
The job of the troops in the inner cordon is to prevent anyone in the search area getting out. They must be put in position very carefully so as not to alert the enemy. The local commander should check that there are no gaps and that the troops know what the search team look like, so that there is no chance of blue-on-blue contacts.

Spetsnaz tactics
The Spetsnaz soldier will have the skills of the urban terrorist and the special forces soldier. His lying-up points and safe house may well be mined and heavily booby-trapped. In addition to automatic weapons, his armoury may include chemical mines and grenades. He or she will not consider surrender as an option. Unfortunately, the first warning you have that you have found the right person may be the burst of fire from an AKSU.

landed in a position from which one could provide fire support for an assault while the third platoon actually made the assault. If time was not critical, such an operation could perfectly well be undertaken using road transport followed by an approach on foot. Bearing in mind the likely shortage of helicopters for home defence operations, you are much more likely to be driving than flying!

Search and destroy operations would not be conducted randomly or speculatively but as a result of firm intelligence. They would be carried out by Regular or TA infantry battalions and possibly composite general re-

Limitations on action
You may have to carry out these types of operation in support of the police in what is technically peacetime, during the transition to war. You cannot act outside the law. Until war is declared the cordoning off of a large residential area and restricting people's freedom by imposing a curfew and searching homes may not be acceptable. These operations invariably involve many innocent and law-abiding civilians. When planning the operation, be sure that the results will justify the risk in exposing troops to sniper attacks, the manpower taken up and the alienation of public opinion.

Secrecy
The whole operation will fail unless you achieve surprise. This usually means you will not be able to do a thorough recce or alert all the civilian authorities beforehand.

Outer cordon
These troops are placed out of range of the target house and prevent any movement into the area using road blocks. The aim is to stop any outside interference with the search operation.

A USAF security team moves out from its bunker. Looking for the enemy will inevitably involve wood clearing operations. Rather than reacting to an attack, it is better to engage the enemy in his patrol base or lying-up point.

If you manage to ambush special purpose forces they will not fight it out with you: their aim is to slope off to fight another day. Here a follow-up group deploys on foot with dogs after an exercise ambush to search and destroy.

serve companies. General service and home service force units would not normally be expected to carry out such a complex operation.

The other likely offensive operation that you might carry out in a Home Defence battalion would be Cordon and Search. This uses more men than a search and destroy operation, and is more likely to be undertaken when looking for terrorists or small parties of lightly armed men who are 'hiding up' somewhere. It can often take place in an urban setting.

Cordon and search

Some men will be inside the cordon searching and they will need immediate protection, and communications with the cordon. The cordon will need to know precisely where the searchers are at all times, and so will also need communications. Some members of the cordon will look inwards to cover the area of search and others will need to be designated to look outwards, not only to protect those who are looking inwards from attack from an unexpected quarter but also in order to engage any enemy who manages to evade the cordon.

You will need mobile reserves to re-

inforce existing key-point guards. Alternatively, a reserve force could be located at a particularly important key point and operate from that location, thus providing an extra degree of security when it is not deployed.

Another important task for Home Defence forces is keeping main routes open to allow the free movement of the armed forces and emergency services. Routes to the ports and to airfields must be kept open during the period when BAOR is being reinforced. Many US forces will use Britain as a staging post before onward movement to Europe, and obviously all British and US troops assigned to NATO must reach Europe if the conventional battle is to be sustained. Routes can be disrupted by air attack, they can be cratered or booby trapped by Spetsnaz forces placing explosive devices, they could be flooded, or they could be clogged with refugees. Bomb disposal teams in particular must be available to ensure that routes are kept open.

In the event of a nuclear attack on the UK, military responsibilities would remain the same except that there would be a much greater emphasis put on military assistance to the civil authorities (MACA) and to the civil power (MACP). MACA would include the restoration of essential services, route clearance and control, reconnaissance and radiac survey, the

distribution of essential supplies and the provision of communications. Obviously in a disaster situation the civil emergency services would be hard pressed to cope, and it would be your task to provide all the additional help that the Army is well equipped to provide.

The role of the police

Primary responsibility for the internal security of the UK, whether in peacetime or in war, lies with the police. Under common law, the armed forces are required, when requested, to come to the assistance of the civil authorities, although the army must at all times respect police primacy in civil matters. In other words, a military commander retains command of his troops at all times but, having responded to a request for MACP, he becomes responsible to the local police commander until the police commander officially hands over operational responsibility to him. The transfer of responsibility should be for the minimum period and within the minimum area but sufficient to allow effective military action to be taken. At the conclusion of military operations, the police commander reassumes operational responsibility.

These are the many mobile tasks which you could be asked to carry out if you become involved in home defence operations. Together with the

All choke points on main supply routes would be targets: these vulnerable points would best be defended by having troops dug in on them. Army units stuck in a massive traffic jam on their way to the channel ports to fight in Germany are effectively out of action.

With the outer and inner cordons in place, a search group moves in in pairs to clear a church. The Spetsnaz will even up the odds with the security forces by the liberal use of automatic weapons and explosives.

The enemy will try to overload the QRF by creating as many incidents as possible, including decoys, while they attack an important target. VCPs will have to be established throughout the operational area.

Route and convoy protection would be a major task in home defence. The Fox armoured car would be used in this role to lend a little armour protection to otherwise completely soft-skinned convoys.

A search and destroy team camouflages its vehicles before moving out. The lack of helicopters means you are limited to vehicles and your feet.

formidable task of guarding KPs, there is much to be done. The Army is, in the final analysis, responsible for the security of the landmass of the British Isles. Invasion by a formed body of enemy troops is very unlikely, but intensive air attack is likely and Spetsnaz troops could be infiltrated in a number of ways. The Army must locate and destroy them as soon as possible after insertion. Failing this, you must prevent them from attacking KPs successfully. You can do this with a combination of static guards, of mobile patrols, and of reserves or quick reaction forces (QRFs). Together they should be able to provide the spider's web that will frustrate the enemy.

Home defence is not, in military terms, a glamorous subject. Compared with Arctic warfare in Norway or mechanised warfare in north-west Europe or amphibious operations in the Falkland Islands, the challenge to a professional soldier may not seem so great. This is not so. First, resources for home defence are meagre: unlike

France and West Germany, who maintain large national service armies in peacetime and therefore can call upon enormous reserves in war, Britain's military manpower resources are limited, so home defence forces will be stretched and tested. Secondly, don't forget that the security of the

home base is vital for the success of all other operations, so successful military operations in Great Britain are as important to the outcome of a conventional war in Europe as the moves and counter-moves of armoured divisions on the Hannover Plain or in the Fulda Gap.

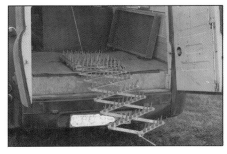

In addition to normal vehicle checkpoints, snap VCPs can be put together using hire vans commandeered by the Army in time of war. The 'lazy tongs' used as a instant backstop in Northern Ireland could find uses closer to home.

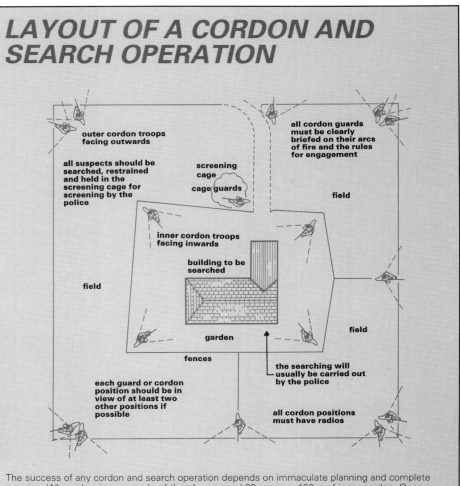

LAYOUT OF A CORDON AND SEARCH OPERATION

outer cordon troops facing outwards

all cordon guards must be clearly briefed on their arcs of fire and the rules for engagement

all suspects should be searched, restrained and held in the screening cage for screening by the police

screening cage

cage guards

field

inner cordon troops facing inwards

building to be searched

field

garden

fences

each guard or cordon position should be in view of at least two other positions if possible

the searching will usually be carried out by the police

field

all cordon positions must have radios

The success of any cordon and search operation depends on immaculate planning and complete surprise. When planning, as a rule of thumb you need 30 men per 100 m of inner cordon. Once the cordon is in place you may be able to thin out depending on the ground and the situation. You must move into position quietly and under cover from the target building. If you are compromised before the cordon is complete, you will have wasted your time.

GETTING A GOOD GROUP

By now you should have absorbed the basics of weapons handling, range safety and the principles of marksmanship. It's time to put all this theorising into practice: now you need to get some range work in.

Your first objective is to shoot a consistent number of groups from which you will be able to accurately zero the sights of your rifle.

Do not hurry your shots. There is no way at this stage that you will be able to shoot a good group rapid-fire. Take plenty of time, resting between shots but taking care not to alter your position in any way. If you are shooting under military supervision, be sure to engage your safety catch when you rest between shots.

Left: You must learn to adjust your firing position so that your rifle is naturally pointing at the target. Shut your eyes and rest a moment, then return the rifle to the aim and open your eyes. If you are in a correct, relaxed position, your sight picture will be near the point of aim.

Split group
This is when you get two small separate groups. Most likely, it means that you have altered your position slightly. Remember not to move your elbows between shots and to test and adjust your position before firing.

Vertical group
If your shots are impacting above or below your point of aim , this will probably mean that there are inconsistencies in the positioning of your eye. Try to keep your head in the correct position and ensure that you are getting the same sight picture for each of your shots.

Diagonal groups
If your shots are high and left of your point of aim this will usually mean that the grip of your trigger hand is loose and the butt of the rifle is coming out of position in the shoulder. If your shots are scattered high and low across the target, the fault will be in your head position. To correct this make sure that your head is properly upright.

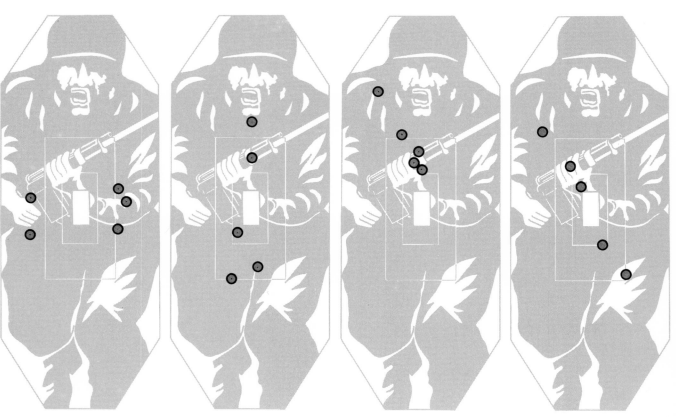

Zeroing your weapon

You will need to fire at least five five-shot groups at 100 yards in the prone position. Measure each group on completion of firing. The group is measured from centre to centre of the extreme spread shot holes; the centre of the group is known as the Mean Point of Impact (MPI). By taking an average of your five or more groups, you will be able to find your correct MPI. Once you have worked out your MPI in relation to your point of aim (POA), you will be able to adjust the sights of your weapon accordingly.

Setting your sights

Most iron sights are quite easy to adjust. Although they are a basically simple device they are capable of good accuracy. Vertical adjustments are made by raising or lowering the foresight; lateral adjustments are made by moving the rearsight from left to right.

Testing and adjusting position

Any change in your position will affect your Mean Point of Impact (MPI) so it is good to get into the habit of testing and adjusting your position before firing.

1 Take aim at your target, then slightly relax your hold. No appreciable alteration of the sight picture should be evident. If you do notice a change of aim, then it is an indication that your position needs some adjustment.

2 Keeping your left elbow firmly in place, move your body to the left or right to correct any lateral errors. For errors in elevation, keep both of your elbows in position and move your body forwards or backwards as necessary. The position of the butt in your shoulder should remain unchanged.

3 To be certain that your position is now correctly adjusted, close your eyes and let the rifle rest. With your eyes still shut return the rifle back to a comfortable position in the shoulder. When you reopen your eyes the sight picture should be either on or very close to the the point of aim. With plenty of practice you should be able to almost automatically adopt a position that requires little or no adjustment.

One shot away

This is when you have a definite four-shot group and one stray shot, or 'flyer'. The most likely cause of this, if your body position is correct, is an error in your sight picture. Try to follow through the shot properly and you will quickly spot your mistake. Concentrate on co-ordinating your aim and trigger release.

Wide group

If your shots are all over the place, looking more like a shotgun blast, it will mean that you are not doing the same thing each time you release a shot. Don't despair: remember your marksmanship principles and try to concentrate harder. With effort, consistency will soon arrive.

Tight group

This is really the type of group you must aim to achieve. Until you can shoot like this, you will be unable to accurately zero your rifle.

Above: Inspecting your group can be a delightful or disappointing surprise. If you have shot badly, do not despair but try to establish what is going wrong. Good shooting comes from practice and dedication. The first step is to shoot a consistently good group. Then you can work to get the group in the right part of the target.

When you zero your rifle at 100 yards you will need to set the rear sight distance at 300m. Some weapons, like the L1A1, have graduated distance settings; others, for instance the M16, have a flip-over rear sight with two apertures, one for two hundred yards and one for four hundred and over. Taking the SLR as an example with the sights set at 300 yards, your mean point of impact when zeroing at 100 yards will be approximately 5 inches above your point of aim.

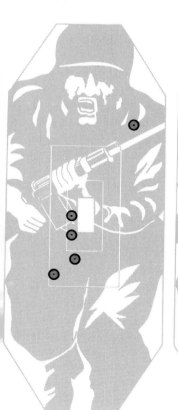

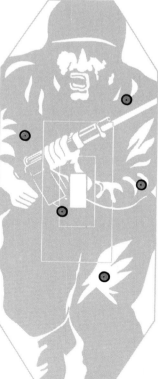

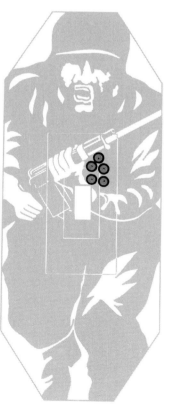

Theory of a group

The size of your group will expand and decrease in direct proportion to the range from which you are firing. For instance, your group shot at 100 yards will be twice the size at 200 yards and three times the size at 300 yards – likewise, at 25 yards it will only be a quarter of the size.

ELEMENTARY APPLICATION OF FIRE

Now that your rifle is properly zeroed and you have mastered the prone position to some degree, it is time to look at some of the factors that will affect your Mean Point of Impact. Unfortunately only a small proportion of your shooting will be conducted under ideal weather conditions at 100 yards. Range, wind, light, ammunition and position will all alter where your rounds impact in relation to where you have actually aimed your shot.

To some degree you will be able to deal with range by quick adjustment of your sights. Even the crudest iron sights have an adjustment for distance that can be made within seconds, although you must still learn to estimate the range of your target accurately. In battle you will not have the opportunity to make any finer adjustment to your sights, so to deal with the other varying conditions you must learn how to compensate for these difficulties by altering your point of aim.

Run down & sight adjustment

Judging your distance to target is a skill that can only really be developed from practical experience. As a bullet's flight or trajectory is curved downward by gravity, it is necessary to adjust your sights for different ranges. On most modern rifles the adjustment is in 100 yd or metre steps from 200 yds/metres to 600 yds/metres. You must not forget to make sight corrections. In competition you only fire from points in multiples of 100 m from the targets. In real life the target could be running towards you and if you do not correct you will miss. Remember also to alter your point of aim when the target is in between the 100 m settings.

Ammo quality

Good ammunition is a very important factor in marksmanship. For competitive use try to use the best match grade ammo at your disposal. This will help to ensure that your Mean Point of Impact is consistent. For battle shooting, make sure that you keep your ammunition clean and free of oil and grit. Avoid any ammunition of dubious origin with an unfamiliar headstamp. For example, some old stocks of Warsaw Pact ammunition use corrosive primers that will begin to seriously damage the bore within hours of use. If by way of accident or desperation you have to use any dodgy ammo be sure to thoroughly strip and clean your weapon.

Above: The amount of smoke from the muzzle tells you the ammunition is a little dodgy or the firer has over-oiled the weapon. Oil in the chamber leads to inconsistent chamber pressures, which can change the mean point of impact.

Lights up, sights up

Changes of lighting can affect your sight picture and cause aiming error. As the individual shooter's eyesight is a variable factor, it is important to make note of any possible alteration in the point of impact caused by excessive or insufficient light – harsh shadows across your target can play havoc with your sight picture. Be sure to concentrate on maintaining a correct sight picture and maintaining consistent eye relief.

A cross wind will displace your shot to the side. A good rifleman must be able to determine the strength of the wind and change his point of aim accordingly. On the range you will be able to judge the speed and direction of any wind by the movement of the range flags: in the field, you must look for natural indications. Look at the direction and force with which any trees, shrubs, grass, dust and smoke are being blown. Even the feel of the wind on your face will help you. Learning to aim off for wind is not easy. You will start by shooting at a Figure 12 target pasted to a six foot screen. Shots off target will be indicated by a white paddle, so that you can correct onto the target. Once you are on target you can move on to shooting at a Figure 11. You will usually start at 300 m and then move back to 500 m.

Optical sights

Optical sights are very useful for correcting on to a target as you will have a better chance of seeing the strike of the bullet: They also cut out the sight alignment problems usually associated with changing light conditions. However, optical sights can restrict your field of vision when in battle.

aiming off for light wind

aiming off for strong wind

point of aim

point of aim

Wind allowance

target
point of impact
point of aim

path of bullet
line of sight

Only strong wind will affect a centrefire rifle bullet at 100 yds, but over this range even a fairly light breeze will alter its flight. This problem will be more evident if you are shooting the 5.56 mm/.223 cartridge, the heaviest bullet head for which is only 70 g. To allow for variation in wind you must learn to 'aim off'. This means that you must aim your shot off the actual target, so that the bullet is blown across onto your intended target. The circle to the right of the centre on the Figure 11 target shows where to aim to compensate for wind speed at 200 yds.

Top left: Signs to look for in determining a strong wind. The circle indicating where you will need to aim to compensate for wind of this strength at 200 yds is now at the very edge of the target. In even stronger wind and at greater distance you will find that you will have to aim completely off the target in proportion to these varying factors.

TAKING UP THE CORRECT POSITIONS

The prone position is by far the most stable shooting support but on active service you will soon discover that circumstances force you to adopt alternatives.

Undergrowth, long grass, man-made structures and the general nature of terrain will often make it impossible to engage targets from the prone position, so you've got to be able to shoot from the kneeling, sitting and standing positions.

These positions are all far less stable. You will find it virtually im-

possible to hold the rifle still enough when aiming to get a perfect sight picture. As a result, you aim at an area of the target rather than a point: the size of this area will depend on the stability of your position, and will decrease in size with practice as your shooting muscles develop and your reflex actions speed up.

Left: This is the most common standing position. Most of the weight is distributed over the leading foot and the feet are placed roughly at 90 degrees to each other with the leading foot aligned with the target. You will not be able to fire long strings of shots like this and should relax into the alert position.

Squatting, alias 'rice paddy prone', is fine for quick reaction shots from behind cover but does not really work for non-oriental soldiers and is very uncomfortable.

Above: Sit on your heel with the elbow of your left arm either in front of or behind the kneecap. Avoid elbow to knee, bone to bone contact, and take the recoil in a rocking motion.

Left: The alternative standing position. The toe of the butt sits in your shoulder and you push your hips out to support your elbow.

To get a good stable position, lock the elbows in with the insides of the knees and dig your heels in. Lean forward into the shot.

SHOOTING POSITIONS

Standing positions
This is used for firing from behind high cover, eg walls and trench positions. It is also used for rapid engagement of targets when advancing. There are two positions:

Position A (Offhand Technique). Your feet should be placed approximately a shoulder width apart, in line with the target, giving maximum balance and comfort. The left hand is placed under the handguard with the left elbow kept directly beneath the rifle. The action of the left hand is to support the weapon by cradling it rather than gripping it. The butt should again be placed high into the shoulder with the right arm kept horizontal. You then turn the body 15 degrees to the right hand side, leaning slightly forwards in the direction of the target.

Position B (Left Hand Supporting Magazine). The placement of the body and right arm is as for the offhand position. Your left hand supports the rifle by cradling the magazine base in the palm of your hand. Your left elbow rests firmly on the top of the left hip for added support.

Neither of these two positions are very recoil resistant and you may experience some difficulties coming back into the correct aim, particularly when engaging in rapid fire.

Kneeling position
Face half right to the target, then kneel on the right knee, making sure it is kept well out to the right. Try if possible to sit on the heel or the side of the foot. The left foot should then be turned inwards to steady the lower left leg and reduce movement. The weight of the body should be shifted over the right heel. When firing from the kneeling position the butt of the rifle needs to be placed high in the shoulder.

Squatting position
This position is useful when firing from shallow water, mud and in open terrain where other positions are not easily adopted. Place your feet a shoulder's width apart and drop down onto your haunches into a natural squatting position. The backs of your thighs should rest on the backs of your calves with the knees bent to their full extent. Avoid too much tension in the thighs, putting strain on the calf muscles. Your body needs to be placed at about 30 degrees towards the line of sight. Adjustment for direction is easily made by moving either the left or right foot to the front or rear as necessary. This position requires some practice to adopt successfully and without too much discomfort. Experimentation with this position may be necessary to ensure that your weight is evenly distributed on the balls of your feet.

The alternative position is to turn your legs in or sit cross-legged. Note the index finger of the left hand pointing towards the target, which can improve your shooting.

High port is used when moving through low cover in an advance to contact, with the weapon instantly ready for use.

On operations your rifle should be in the alert position most of the time when moving. The rifle can very quickly be brought up into the aim to fire a shot from standing or kneeling.

Sitting position
The sitting position is a good option for a number of situations: firing from hillsides and low vegetation, engaging moving targets at quite short ranges, and it is an excellent position for night ambushes as it offers fairly good concealment and some comfort when waiting for long periods of time. Sit with your legs crossed or apart, making sure that your feet are in a comfortable position. The rifle should be held in the same way as in the kneeling position except with the elbows in front of or on the inside of the knees.

CLOSE QUARTER BATTLE POSITIONS

When moving cross country, through woodland, or when patrolling in rural and urban areas, an enemy may open fire and attack at close quarters. It is imperative that you are able to react quickly in such a situation and be in a position that allows you to return fast and accurate fire. It is therefore essential that you carry your rifle in a manner that gives a state of readiness and suitability for the terrain over which you are moving.

High port
Bring the rifle up to a diagonal hold across the body. Your left hand is on the handguard and your right hand on the pistol grip. The barrel is pointed upwards. The selector switch is put on the fire position and the trigger finger is rested on the trigger itself. Great care must be taken

The low port. The weapon can quickly be swung down across the body making ready and sliding the safely off at the same time.

The cradle carry is designed to be a non-aggressive stance, which still allows you to get a round off fairly quickly.

not to put pressure on the trigger, and the safety must be engaged when necessary. This position is used when going through vegetation and when crossing obstacles. If you should trip or stumble in this position your rifle will not get entangled and the muzzle will not get full of dirt or point at any of your comrades.

The alert position
The left hand is on the handguard and the right hand is on the pistol grip with your trigger finger resting on the trigger. The butt of the rifle is placed low in the shoulder with the muzzle pointed at a 45 degree angle towards the ground. The selector switch is put on the fire position. Again, great care must be taken to use this position safely – be sure that you never muzzle sweep anyone who may be to your front. The safety must be engaged when crossing obstacles.

The cradle carry
This is an alternative to the alert position and is used when you are wearing a fragmentation vest or any other bulky body armour. Hold the rifle as you would in the alert position but allow the butt to rest on the outside of the right arm with the weight cradled by the elbow.

The low port
This position is used for internal security operations when one hand is needed for searching personnel, checking documents or the moving of barriers. Your right hand holds the pistol grip with the finger outside the trigger guard. The barrel is pointed upwards with the base of the butt resting on the waist belt or hip. The selector switch is put on safe.

Into the Boonies with the M48

The M48 Main Battle Tank has seen action all over the world from the Middle East to Asia and was the most powerful armoured vehicle used in Vietnam by American forces. Modernisation kits now on offer seem likely to prolong the M48's career to the end of the century. Christened the Patton after the most famous US tank commander of World War II, the M48 was designed hurriedly and rushed into production in 1953, after the Korean war had exposed the US Army's alarming shortage of modern tanks.

Early M48s were plagued with teething troubles because of the tank's hasty introduction to service. And, although a sound vehicle with reasonable armour protection and a relatively powerful armament, it suffered from an embarassingly short range (just 70 miles) and still used the complicated stereoscopic rangefinder that had defeated so many tank crews on the M47. The rangefinder allowed the 90-mm main armament to fire accurately to over 1500 m, but it was anything but soldier-proof.

Several successive variants improved the design: the M48A2 had a fuel injection engine, which more than doubled its range, but only with the M48A3 did the US Army finally get what it needed. Diesel powered and with a coincidence rangefinder, the M48A3 was the version taken to Vietnam by 1st Battalion 69th Armored in 1966.

Inside the M48

The layout of the M48 is entirely conventional. The driver sits in the centre of the hull front, and the commander and gunner sit in the turret to the right of the main armament. On the other side of the gun sits the loader. The M48 was the first American tank to abandon the fifth crewman, who used to man a hull machine gun and act as a spare driver or radio operator. Most M48s have an infra-red/white light searchlight mounted above the 90-mm gun. This

is of limited use today but 2/34th Armored used theirs to spring night ambushes on Viet Cong supply vessels on the Saigon river.

The main armament of the M48A3 is an M41 90-mm gun, with a distinctive blast deflector on the end of the barrel. With a maximum effective range of 2,500 metres it fires armour piercing rounds, smoke, canister and high explosive anti-tank (HEAT)

A US Marine Corps M48 flamethrower tank blasts liquid fire in Vietnam during 1967. The Marines found tanks armed with flamethrowers very useful fighting the Japanese on Okinawa, but only made limited use of armour in Vietnam. Designated M67, the flamethrower version of the M48 is no longer in service.

shells. The latter are more effective at penetrating the armour of enemy tanks, but armour-penetrating (AP) rounds are more accurate. The driver is surrounded by ammunition – 19 rounds are stored on his left and 11 on his right. Eight more are on the turret floor, and another 16 around the turret ring. Israeli combat experience has revealed that storing such large amounts of ammunition in the turret is a recipe for a catastrophic secondary explosion should the tank suffer a penetrative hit on the turret.

The M48 in Vietnam

Senior American officers in Vietnam opposed the deployment of M48s in-country, believing that the terrain was unsuitable and armoured units should stick to M113 APCs and light tanks like the M41.

But, where the tank was used in Vietnam, it proved surprisingly effective. The M48's armour enabled it to survive repeated hits from enemy anti-tank weapons, although the concussion and blast damage from a non-penetrative hit could be traumatic for

the crew. Some USMC M48s recorded 15 hits each from B-40 rocket-propelled grenades, and crews had to be changed at least once a day. M48s of the US Marine Corps supported Marine foot soldiers in the 26 days of close-quarter fighting during the battle for Hue in 1968. The tanks found themselves in great demand: their firepower was vital in knocking out enemy strongpoints, and tanks

A USMC M48 rumbles into Hué to support the Marines infantry. The tanks were so vital to the Marines that although crew members were rotated to allow them to catch some sleep, the vehicles remained almost constantly in action.

Inside the M48

The M48A3 medium tank was deployed to Vietnam, where it proved highly successful despite widespread prejudice about using 'heavy' armour in the poor tank country of South East Asia. The destruction of the French Mobile Group 100 by the Viet Minh had convinced many American commanders that tank units would be too vulnerable to guerrilla ambush:

Commander
When using the main armament, the commander uses the co-incidence range finder which is fairly accurate at up to 4000 metres and has ×10 magnification.

.50-cal Browning machine-gun

Loader
Unlike his unfortunate counterpart in a T-54/55, the loader in an M48 has reasonable amount of room and can use his rig** hand to pick up the shells

Turret ammunitio
There are eight rea** rounds in the turret, shells stored vertica** around the turret ri** another eight on the**

M1 cupola
This rotates independently through 360 degrees and has five vision blocks and a sight for the .50-cal Browning machine-gun.

Turret A single-piece casting, the M48's turret is not ballistically well shaped. It is 120mm thick at the front and only 76mm thick along the sides.

Gunner
The gunner has a ×8 periscope and a ×8 telescope slaved to the main armament.

Extra armour
Many tank crews fixed sections of track on the turret sides as an extra defence against RPG-7 anti-tank rockets.

Hull ammunition
Nineteen rounds are stowed to the left of the driver and 11 on his right.

120-mm hull front armour

Driver
Seated in the centre of the hull, the driver has a single piece hatch which swings open to the right and is cut off from the rest of the crew.

Men of the 9th US Marine Regiment advance through a clearing near Cam Lo in 1967. An M48 lends its weight to the defence of the landing zone as a CH-46 helicopter arrives to evacuate the wounded.

routinely used up their 90-mm ammunition in a few hours.

There was only one occasion when American armour encountered enemy tanks during the Vietnam war. The Ben Het Special Forces Camp in II Corps overlooked the Ho Chi Minh trail where the borders of Vietnam, Laos and Cambodia meet. Elements from 1st Battalion, 69th Armor were stationed in the area, one platoon in the camp itself. On the night of 3 March 1969 the camp was shelled, and the garrison clearly heard the clatter of tracks and the sounds of heavy engines. An anti-tank mine exploded outside the perimeter and tracked a PT-76 amphibious light tank.

There followed an exchange of rounds between as yet unidentified enemy tanks and the M48s in the

Right: The two US tank battalions in South Korea are the only regular units to retain the M48. They drive M48A5s, in common with the South Korean armoured formations. With a 105-mm gun, modernised fire control and new engine, the M48A5 is a substantial improvement over the original M48.

-red/white light chlight
can illuminate targets 2000 metres away of course, also inates the tank. It was l in Vietnam where uerrillas lacked infra-etectors.

M41 90-mm gun
The 90-mm gun can easily be distinguished by the prominent blast deflector. Firing fixed ammunition, it is roughly equivalent in hitting power to the Soviet 100-mm gun in the T-54/55.

Drive sprocket
This is at the rear and the idler is at the front.

Return rollers

Rubber tyred road wheels

Escape hatch
Underneath the hull there is a single escape hatch for the crew to bail out of and hopefully avoid the attentions of enemy machine-gunners.

camp. American flares helped both sides – one M48 was struck by an 85-mm shell, which killed the driver and loader. Firing continued even after the US tanks ran out of armour-piercing shell and switched to high explosive (HE) with concrete-piercing fuses. The North Vietnamese eventually ceased fire and, at first light, a sweep of the battlefield revealed two knocked out PT-76s and a brewed-up APC that no-one remembered engaging.

With the ARVN

Although the North Vietnamese were to employ armour in increasing quantities during the war, they never clashed with American tank units again. However, M48s in South Vietnamese service continued the fight.

The stand of the 20th ARVN tank regiment near Quang Tri in 1972 was a special South Vietnamese success story.

Rushed forward against a tide of North Vietnamese troops pouring over the DMZ, three squadrons of M48s deployed to defend the Dong Ha bridge. They engaged a mixed column of enemy armour at a range of about 3,000-m, destroying two T-54s and nine PT-76s. Unable to locate the South Vietnamese firing positions, the NVA armour retreated hurriedly. A week later, the regiment destroyed 16 T-54s and captured a T-59 along National Highway 9.

The ARVN M48s continued to inflict serious damage on enemy armoured forces, despite losing several of their number to AT-3 'Sagger' anti-tank missiles. The M48s of the 20th Regiment were defeated only after they ran out of fuel, ammunition and infantry support.

With the exception of that one night at Ben Het, American M48s fought their battles against enemy infantry. The HE round from the 90-mm gun was far from ideal in the point-blank-range battles that US armoured forces usually found themselves in.

The crews' favourite anti-personnel shell was a canister round, which converted the 90-mm gun into a giant shotgun. Containing either 1,280 shot or between 5,000 and 10,000 steel darts called flechettes, these 'beehive' rounds were devastatingly effective. On one occasion, when the beehives ran out, a troop from 5th Cavalry fired HE shells with delayed fuses in front of their ambushers. The shells ricochetted before detonating, producing an effective airburst.

Mines were the main source of

armour casualties during the Vietnam war. Several M48s were fitted with mine-rollers, but they were slow, ineffective in soft ground, and often wrecked when they detonated a mine. A more dramatic solution was the 'Thunder Run': a night patrol by armoured forces along routes that the Viet Cong habitually mined. A column would speed down the road, indiscriminately firing into the surrounding area. This undoubtedly frustrated some attempts at laying mines but was hardly a comprehensive solution.

Around the world

The M48 was supplied to many US allies and played a crucial role in the Israeli victory in the 1967 Six-Day War. Together with British Centurions, M48s spearheaded the Israeli blitzkrieg that routed the Egyptian Army in Sinai. Engaging Soviet-supplied T-54/55 Main Battle Tanks, the Israeli M48s performed well. They were far more reliable than the Arab armour, and their 90-mm HEAT rounds easily penetrated the T-54's armour.

The M60 was, originally, no more than an M48 with a new turret that had a better ballistic profile and a 105-mm gun. As they acquired M60s, the Israelis improved their M48s to M60 standard by fitting their version of the M68 105-mm gun and installing a 12-cylinder Continental diesel engine.

The US Army upgraded its M48 fleet in much the same way, and the resulting M48A5 is the ultimate M48 in American service. It took five years from 1975 to modernise the 1,600 or so M48s still in American service, and today they serve with the National Guard. They are scheduled to be replaced by M60s as regular armoured units receive the M1 Abrams. By 1989 they may no longer be in US service.

The M48 was the mainstay of the post-war West German army until the Bundeswehr received enough of their

own Leopard tanks. However, the M48s soldiered on and 650 were rebuilt to M48A5 standard during the late 1970s. Improvements included an L7 105-mm gun, as fitted to the Leopard 1: passive night vision equipment and a new commander's cupola. Some 170 modernisation kits were supplied to the Turkish army, to upgrade its M48 fleet.

Soldiering on

The M48 continues to serve in many armies, and several German and American companies are offering modernisation kits to prolong the tank's useful life. Greece has modernised its force of about 600 M48s to

The summer of '69: an M48A3 of 10th Cavalry lies in sweltering temperatures with a poncho rigged over the turret and deck chairs on the engine deck. American tanks in Vietnam were often cluttered with kit, but this crew are going for the record.

Battlefield Evaluation: comparing

M48

The M48 served the Israelis very well in 1967 and 1973, and those tanks deployed to Vietnam acquitted themselves nobly. The M48 had no outstanding advantages of design over contemporary Soviet vehicles: it was simply better built. As the 90-mm main armament became outdated most M48s acquired standard 105-mm guns, and there are various modernisation kits available to bring the M48 up to M60 standard.

Specification:
Crew: 4
Combat weight: 45 tonnes
Road speed: 42 km/h
Power to weight ratio: 18 hp/tonne
Length: 6.7 m
Height: 3.1 m
Armament: 1×90-mm gun; 1×12.7-mm and 1×7.62-mm machine-guns

Assessment
Firepower	★★★
Protection	★★★
Age	★★★★★
Worldwide users	★★★

An M48 of the West German army is part of 'Aggressor' forces during joint exercises in 1973.

Centurion

Appearing before the M48, the Centurion was superior in everything except speed. Both tanks had problems with unreliable engines in early production versions, and once this was solved both became effective vehicles. Centurions and M48s were the main strength of the Israeli tank forces during the Six Day War, Super-Shermans and AMX-13s lacking the armour protection to take on T-55s.

Specification:
Crew: 4
Combat weight: 52 tonnes
Road speed: 35 km/h
Power to weight ratio: 12.5 hp/tonne
Length: 7.8 m
Height: 3 m
Armament: 1×105-mm gun; 1×12.7-mm machine-gun; 2×7.62-mm machine-guns

Assessment
Firepower	★★★★
Protection	★★★★
Age	★★★★★
Worldwide users	★★

The Centurion partnered the M48 in the great Israeli tank victories of 1967 and 1973.

T-54/55

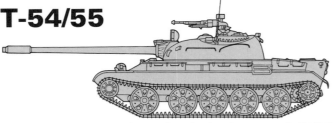

Just as the M48 showed the influence of wartime American armour, the T-54/55 followed up the excellent tanks produced by the Russians during the war. Whereas the M48 was high, heavy and roomy, the T-54 followed the opposite route to produce a potentially more powerful tank, but 25 per cent lighter. Only the poor fire control equipment and lack of crew comfort prevent it completely outclassing the M48.

Specification:
Crew: 4
Combat weight: 36 tonnes
Road speed: 50 km/h
Power to weight ratio: 16 hp/tonne
Length: 6.45 m
Height: 2.4 m
Armament: 1×100-mm gun; 1×12.7-mm and 1×7.62-mm machine-guns

Assessment
Firepower	★★★
Protection	★★★★
Age	★★★★★
Worldwide users	★★★★★

Far lighter but better protected, the T-54/55 is a match for an M48 given similar crews.

M48A3 standard; Spain, Pakistan and Turkey all have large fleets of M48A5s. The M48 will remain South Korea's MBT well into the 1990s. Its Hyundai-built economy version of the M1 Abrams is only now entering series production.

The M48 is certainly not an outstanding tank. It is substantially bigger and heavier than its Soviet contemporary, the T-54, but has little more armour protection. However, it has proved itself as a reliable piece of kit, and its combat record is good. As the price of a modern MBT spirals ever upward, an upgraded M48 is an attractive option to the smaller military powers.

Mines continued to be the main source of AFV losses in Vietnam, and many methods were tried to counter them. Here an M48 mine roller from 10th Cavalry trundles down Highway 19 in 1970. The rollers and sweeps did not prove successful.

the M48 with its rivals

M47

The M47 was the first completely new tank introduced to the US Army after World War II. Its main claim to fame was its stereoscopic rangefinder which, when it was working, gave the M47 a massive advantage in long-range gunnery. The M47 was rushed into service in 1951 as the US Army desperately sought to catch up the Soviet Union's superiority in quantity and quality of main battle tanks. The M48 replaced it shortly afterwards and most M47s were shipped to American allies.

Specification:
Crew: 5
Combat weight: 46 tonnes
Road speed: 48km/h
Power to weight ratio: 17.5hp/tonne
Length: 6.35m
Height: 3m
Armament: 1×90-mm gun; 1×12.7-mm and 1×7.62-mm machine-guns

Assessment
Firepower	★★★
Protection	★★★
Age	★★★★★
Worldwide users	★★★

This M47 hulk has recently appeared as a gate guardian at the Support Weapons Wing at Netheravon.

M60

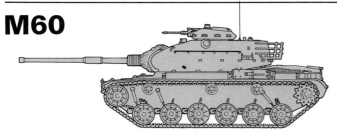

The M60 prototype was basically an M48A2 fitted with a diesel engine, a modified version of the British L7 105-mm tank gun. The first production vehicle introduced a new flat glacis and a larger cupola. The old M48 style turret was soon replaced as inadequate to withstand a hit from a T-62. As the M60 replaced the M48 'medium tank' and the M103 'heavy tank' it was soon referred to as a 'main battle tank', a name which has now passed into NATO-speak.

Specification:
Crew: 4
Combat weight: 52 tonnes
Road speed: 48km/h
Power to weight ratio: 14hp/tonne
Length: 6.9m
Height: 3.27m
Armament: 1×105-mm gun; 1×12.7-mm and 1×7.62-mm machine-guns

Assessment
Firepower	★★★★
Protection	★★★★
Age	★★★★
Worldwide users	★★★★

By replacing M48s and M103 heavy tanks, the M60 led to the phrase 'Main Battle Tank'.

S-tank

The Swedish S-tank was designed above all as a reaction against tanks of the M48 type and their high silhouettes. The solution of a turretless vehicle, pivoting on its tracks to aim the gun, offers a very small target. Both the USA and USSR are currently testing vehicles which follow the S-tank concept: the Americans are looking for an air-portable light tank, but the Russians are experimenting with a full-blown MBT fitted with a 135-mm gun.

Specification:
Crew: 3
Combat weight: 40 tonnes
Road speed: 50km/h
Power to weight ratio: 18hp/tonne
Length: 7.04m
Height: 2.14m
Armament: 1×105-mm gun; 3×7.62-mm machine-guns

Assessment
Firepower	★★★★
Protection	★★★★
Age	★★★★
Worldwide users	★

The S-tank alternative to tanks of the classic type may yet take over as both superpowers test turretless MBTs.

Killdozer: The Centurion AVRE

The Centurion AVRE (Assault Vehicle Royal Engineer) is the most powerful armoured engineer vehicle used by the British Army. The Centurion medium tank was introduced at the end of World War II, and there are several specialist versions of the tank still in service. This is the 105 AVRE: a Centurion tank formerly used by the Royal Artillery for forward observation, now converted to the armoured-engineer role.

Since the late 1970s the Soviet Army has substantially improved its battlefield mobility. The versatile BMP series is fast replacing the BTR-60 as a troop carrier and the vast majority of artillery is now mechanised. Equally important to NATO is the new introduced BM-27 multi-barrel rocket launcher, which is capable of hurling a cocktail of anti-armour and anti-personnel mines over 32 km.

As a direct result the British Army has had to reappraise many of its own support tactics. Previously it could hope to move its reserve troops around the rear areas in comparative safety, but in the future whole brigades could be cut off by minefields laid by the BM-27, while fast-moving Soviet forces overrun the front line.

Routes now have to be cleared and vehicles recovered and repaired faster than ever before if whole elements of I(Br) Corps are not to be caught in the pincer movements that sections of the Soviet 3 Shock Army facing them are busy practising.

Unfortunately, the British Army lacks the resources to introduce a complete new series of weapon systems to combat these Soviet tactics. It has been forced instead to expand its fleet of engineer vehicles based on the old Centurion tank.

Right: The original AVRE, now designated 165 AVRE, is easily distinguished by its stubby 165-mm demolition gun. This fires monstrous HESH rounds to demolish anything from houses to pillboxes or small bridges. The Centurion is fun to drive, with plenty of scope for crash gear changes, but on the modern battlefield its lack of NBC protection is a serious drawback.

Development of the system

Centurion has had a long and successful career within the British Army and has seen action all over the world. Early model Centurions arrived in Germany during 1945 but were too late to see action. The Centurion Mk III was used by British forces in Korea and later models saw service in Egypt, Israel, Iraq, Jordan and the Lebanon, and with the Indian Army in the Indo-Pakistan War and with the Australians in Vietnam.

Throughout its life the Centurion has been constantly up-armoured and upgunned. Originally armed with the 17-pounder gun, it then took on the 20-pounder with the introduction of the Mk IKII in 1947/48. Later the tank was equipped with the 105mm L7 series gun subsequently adopted throughout NATO.

Other improvements included increased fuel capacity (Mk VI), contra-rotating commander's cupola (Mk VIII), and improved stowage (Mk VI/I). All models of the Centurion, including the latest engineering variants, use the same basic engine and transmission.

The Centurion powerpack

All variants mount a Rolls-Royce Meteor Mk IVB 12-cylinder liquid-cooled petrol engine placed (together with the Merritt-Brown Z51R transmission with five forward and two reverse gears) at the rear of the hull. Capable of generating 650bhp at 2,550rpm, these give the vehicle a maximum road speed of 35kph (21mph), a road range of 176km (110 miles) and the ability to climb gradients of 60 per cent.

The suspension is of the Horstman type, consisting of three units each with two pairs of road wheels sprung by a single set of concentric coil springs, with a drive sprocket at the rear and an idler at the front.

A tank for the sappers

The most popular and versatile variant of the Centurion on active service today is the Mk V Assault Vehicle Royal Engineer or AVRE. Developed to replace the Churchill AVRE, the first prototype was completed in 1957 and production began in the early 1960s. Although many of the roles of the AVRE have now been taken over by the Combat Engineer Tractor, the Centurion AVRE continues to be deployed with 32 Armoured Engineer Regiment in Germany, The Regiment, an integral part of 1 (Br) Corps, has three squadrons each with three troops with three AVREs per troop.

The AVRE is based on a standard all-welded Centurion tank hull with a cast turret and roof welded in position. Originally all AVREs were armed with the short-nosed 165 mm demolition gun designed specifically to destroy pill-boxes and other battlefield targets. But since 1984 a few models, converted from the now redundant Royal Artillery forward observation vehicle, have retained the standard 105 mm L7 tank gun. To date these have been fitted with mine ploughs (but not dozer blades) and have been seen towing various trailers including the Giant Viper mine clearing apparatus. It is possible that this variant has been introduced specifically to counter the threat of rocket launched mine fields from the Soviet BM-27.

Arms and equipment

The conventional 165 mm gun can fire a 29 kg (63.8 lb) HESH (High Explosive Squash Head) projectile a distance of 2,400 metres (1.5 miles) although due to its very low muzzle velocity its effective range is no more than 1,200 metres (0.75 miles).

One 0.30 Browning machine gun is mounted to the left of the main armament, and another above the commander's cupola, to provide limited anti-aircraft protection.

The huge hydraulically-operated dozer blade mounted at the front of the hull can move 229 cubic metres of soil per hour, sufficient to maintain a reasonable rate of advance for a single column of armoured vehicles.

A jib can be mounted at the front of the hull for lifting purposes. A rotatable hook, which can be electronically jettisoned if necessary, is fitted to the rear for towing a 7.5-ton four-wheeled trailer.

To complete the AVRE's versatility a fascine cradle, capable of carrying a length of Class 60 trackway, is

165-mm demolition gun
Designed to deal with close-range targets only, the demolition gun is inaccurate over 1200 metres but its 29 kg HESH (High Explosive Squash Head) rounds are devastating against field defences or buildings and would clobber any tank that got in the way.

Co-driver
The Centurion was the last tank in British service to include a fifth crew member

Fascine cradle
The old wooden fascine bundles in use since Roman times are now supplemented by plastic tubing, which is actually stronger. The cradle carries a bundle of fascines about 1.8 metres in diameter.

Dozer blade

Inside the Centurion AVRE

The AVRE can clear obstacles off a road or knock a house down on top of it; in fact, it is potentially the most destructive armoured vehicle in the Army. This is the 165 AVRE fitted with the standard dozer blade and fascine carrying cradle.

Road wheels
The suspension consists of three units each of two road wheels.

Side skirts
These provide additional protection against small calibre HEAT warheads the RPG-7 rocket-launcher

mounted above the dozer. The fascine, a 1.8 metre thick bundle of wood or plastic piping, can be dropped into an anti-tank ditch either manually or with the aid of electrically fired blow-out pins. Alternatively it can be split up, to provide 18 metres of trackway capable of supporting the latest generation of main battle tanks.

Unlike the more modern Combat Engineer Tractor (CET) the AVRE is neither proofed against nuclear, biological and chemical attack, nor capable of deep fording.

The long rack above the dozer blade is used to carry fascines: large bundles of plastic piping used to fill in ditches too wide for a tank to cross.

al Browning
old machine-guns are
replaced by GPMGs.

Gunner

er
mmunition is very
and relatively few can
ried.

Commander

Commander's cupola
This can be traversed 360
degrees independently of
the main turret, and has
seven periscopes for
observation and a sight
linked to that of the gunner.

Wire stowage basket

*British armoured regiments still use the
Centurion armoured recovery vehicle,
which first entered service in 1957. Its
winch can pull up to 90,000 kg using
snatch blocks.*

**Cast manganese steel
tracks**

Drive sprocket
The idler is at the front,
concealed here by the side
skirts.

The Armoured Recovery Vehicle

The standard Centurion tank hull has also been converted into the Mk 2 Armoured Recovery Vehicle or ARV. First introduced in 1956, the vehicle is still, despite its age, in service with the British Army, which has four per armoured regiment, as well as with the Danish, Indian, Dutch, Israeli and South African Armed forces.

The driver sits at the front right, with the remaining three crew members and winch compartment in the centre. Engine and transmission are at

the rear. The commander's cupola, on top of the crew compartment, can be traversed manually through 360 degrees and is fitted with a 0.30 Browning machine-gun.

The huge winch, which is provided with 137 metres of 88.9 mm diameter rope, has a capacity of 31,000 kg. Snatch blocks can increase this to a massive 90,000 kg.

A Rolls-Royce B 80 petrol engine developing 160 hp at 3,750 rpm drives an electric generator to power the winch motor. During recovery, which usually takes place with the winch

cable leading out to the rear, large spades attached behind the engine compartment can be lowered to improve stability.

The Bridgelayer

Although no longer in service with the British Army, the Bridgelayer remains operational with Canadian and Australian forces. A class 80 bridge, capable of transporting the heaviest tank, is carried horizontally over a Mk V Centurion chassis and launched through an angle of 180 degrees over the vehicle front. The single-span bridge, which takes only two minutes to lay and four minutes to recover, can be fitted with a hand-laid centre deck between the trackways to let light, wheeled vehicles (such as the ubiquitous Land Rover) pass over it.

The Royal Marines use five BARVs (Beach Armoured Recovery Vehicles) to push grounded landing craft into deeper water and pull disabled vehicles ashore. There are only four crew, and one is a trained diver who can connect tow cables underwater to damaged vehicles.

The future

Vickers, in conjunction with Marconi Command and Control Systems, have developed a series of retrofit modifications to bring the Centurion right up to date. A specially designed General Motors 12V-71T diesel engine, developing 720 bhp, has been introduced to enhance the vehicle's range and mobility.

The crew compartment has been completely revamped by the addition of plug-in modules and solid-state components. The commander's cupola has been redesigned and fitted with a dual magnification (x1 and x15) sight, and a Marconi gun control and stabilisation system has been intro-

Battlefield Evaluation: comparing

Centurion AVRE

Deployed with 32 Armoured Engineer Regiment in the British Army of the Rhine, the Centurion AVRE is now supplemented by the CET but remains an important vehicle. From 1984 the Royal Artillery handed over the Centurions it used to use as forward observation posts, and these have now been added to the AVRE fleet.

Specification: (165 AVRE)
Crew: 5
Combat weight: 51.8 tonnes
Road speed: 34 km/h
Length: 8.68 m
Height: 3 m
Armament: 1×165-mm demolition gun: 2×7.62-mm machine-guns

Assessment
Firepower ★★★★
Versatility ★★★★★
Age ★★★★★
Worldwide users ★

Despite the arrival of the purpose-built CET the AVRE remains an important engineer vehicle.

AMX 30 EBG

The AMX 30 EBG uses the same chassis as the AMX 30 bridgelayer but with the engine, suspension and transmission of the more modern AMX 30 B2. Fitted with a dozer blade able to dig 120 cubic metres of earth per hour, the EBG also carries a scarifier. When this is swung into position the EBG can slowly reverse along a road, ripping it up as it goes along. The EBG has four tubes for launching mines, a demolition charge launcher and a demolition gun firing a 17 kg round.

Specification:
Crew: 3
Combat weight: 38 tonnes
Road speed: 65 km/h
Length: 7.9 m
Height: 2.94 m
Armament: 1×142-mm demolition gun; 1×7.62-mm machine-gun; 4×mine projectors

Assessment
Firepower ★★★★★
Versatility ★★★★★
Age ★★★
Worldwide users ★

The French army equivalent is the EBG, a development of the AMX-30 series of medium tanks.

Leopard AEV

Based on the chassis of the Leopard 1 Main Battle Tank, the ARV can rip up roads, dig holes, prepare or remove battlefield obstacles, excavate AFV firing positions and prepare river banks for water crossing. The West German army has some 37 Leopard ARVs and the vehicle is also used by Belgium, Italy and the Netherlands. The crane can lift up to 20 tonnes and the maximum tractive effort of the winch is 70 tonnes.

Specification:
Crew: 3
Combat weight: 40.8 tonnes
Road speed: 65 km/h
Length: 7.98 m
Height: 2.69 m
Armament: 1×7.62-mm machine-gun in bow; 1×7.62-mm AA machine-gun

Assessment
Firepower ★
Protection ★★★★
Age ★★★★
Worldwide users ★★

The Leopard AEV is a capable engineer vehicle fitted with a large auger to drill holes.

duced to replace the obsolete thermionic equipment.

Vickers are selling any combination of these modern facilities in such a way that potential user countries can complete the retro-fitting in their own workshops. To date, Switzerland, Sweden and India have shown a distinct interest. It seems likely that modernised Centurions will continue in operation for the foreseeable future.

The fate of the engineering variants however is less certain. As Britain, the only major user, introduces more Challenger tanks, an increasing number of Chieftain chassis will become available. Steps have already been taken to adapt these into AVREs, bridgelayers and recovery vehicles.

Tasks like obstacle clearance and digging fire positions are increasingly left to the CET as AVREs acquire mineclearing kit to tackle the potential threat from Warsaw Pact air- and artillery-launched minefields. This 165 AVRE carries the Pearson mine plough.

the Centurion AVRE with its rivals

IMR

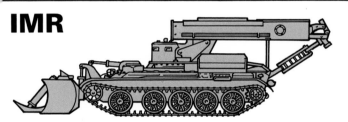

The IMR, based on the chassis of the T-55, is the standard Soviet armoured engineer vehicle and is widely used throughout the Warsaw Pact. Unlike the Centurion, EBG and M728, the IMR has no demolition capacity. The tank turret is replaced by a hydraulically operated crane with 360 degree traverse and two pincer-type grabs for ripping up trees and small obstacles. Its dozer blade can be used straight or in 'V' configuration, but is unable to angle doze.

Specification:
Crew: 2
Combat weight: 34 tonnes
Road speed: 48 km/h
Length: 6.45 m
Height: 2.48 m
Armament: none

Assessment
Firepower —
Versatility ***
Age *****
Worldwide users ****

The IMR may look as if it escaped from Thunderbirds, but it is an important Warsaw Pact vehicle.

CET

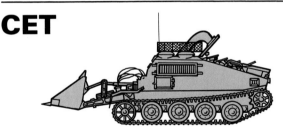

The first CET was accepted by the British Army in 1978 and it has proved itself to be a very useful engineer vehicle indeed. Designed to provide integral engineer support to BAOR battles groups, the CET is used to excavate firing positions, move disabled vehicles out of the way, repair and maintain roads and prepare or remove battlefield obstacles. On top of the hull it has a rocket-propelled, self-emplacing earth anchor.

Specification:
Crew: 2
Combat weight: 17.7 tonnes
Road speed: 56 km/h
Length: 5.3 m
Height: 2.83 m
Armament: 1×7.62-mm machine-gun

Assessment
Firepower *
Versatility ****
Age ***
Worldwide users *

The CET is a very versatile vehicle and, unlike the AVRE, it includes an NBC system.

M728

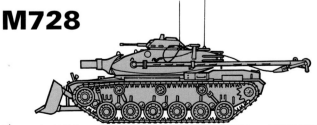

The standard US Army combat engineer vehicle, the M728 is an M60A1 MBT with its 105-mm gun replaced by a 165-mm demolition gun which fires a HESH round. The vehicle is fitted with a dozer blade and carries an 'A' frame over the turret, which can lift up to 15 tonnes. A 7.62-mm machine-gun is mounted co-axially with the main armament and the commander's cupola carries a .50-cal Browning.

Specification:
Crew: 4
Combat weight: 53.2 tonnes
Road speed: 48 km/h
Length: 8.92 m
Height: 3.2 m
Armament: 1×165-mm demolition gun; 1×7.62-mm machine-gun; 1×.50-cal machine-gun

Assessment
Firepower ****
Versatility *****
Age ****
Worldwide users ***

The M728 is the US equivalent of the AVRE and also carries a 165-mm demolition gun.

ROCK ON WITH THE RUGER

Sturm, Ruger & Company of Southport, Connecticut, USA, appeared in the late 1940s with a simple .22 automatic pistol which rapidly acquired a high reputation for accuracy and reliability. Some years later, when the mania for single-action Western-style revolvers was sweeping America, they stepped in where Colt failed to tread and produced a range of excellent revolvers. After that they went on to make shotguns and hunting rifles, and rarely did they put a foot wrong.

When the 5.56-mm (.223) cartridge began to make itself felt in the military world, Ruger looked at the rifles on the commercial market and realised that they were entirely military-oriented, and that something a trifle less aggressive in appearance might well be popular. Since the recoil of the 5.56-mm cartridge is fairly low, and because the evergreen M1 carbine was always in demand, Ruger had the happy idea to weld two together, producing a light semi-automatic rifle similar to the M1 carbine and chambered for the 5.56-mm round. The result, introduced in 1973, was the Mini-14, so called because in many respects it was a miniaturised version of the contemporary US Army M14 rifle.

Military selective fire versions are available, with a cyclic rate of fire of around 750 rounds per minute. At the top is the AC 556, with the snubby AC 556k cut-down folding stock model below it.

The Mini 14 is a well thought-out, fast-handling, lightweight assault rifle which has made some well deserved inroads into the police and military market.

Many police forces in the US and UK, notably SWAT teams and the RUC, have adopted the Mini 14 in 5.56mm for urban counter-sniping. A wide range of after-market accessories including silencers are produced by various companies cashing in on the Mini's success.

It was not, though, a simple matter of scaling down the well-known Garand action. The chamber pressure of the 5.56-mm cartridge at about 3,650 kg/cm^2 is higher than that of the 7.62-mm NATO cartridge at 3,515 kg/cm^2, and the forces involved are still very high. The bolt is the standard rotating pattern developed by Garand for the M1, but the gas system is somewhat different.

Gas system

The cocking handle is on the right of the breech, forming part of the operating rod. On pulling this back, a cam cut on the inner surface of the operating rod causes the bolt to rotate and unlock. Further movement of the

The M14 service rifle was arguably the most accurate self loading service rifle ever produced, with scoped accurised versions continuing in service as sniper rifle known as the M21. Ruger have borrowed some of the design features of two success stories, the M14 and the M1 carbine, to produce a triumph all of their own.

cocking handle opens the bolt, and it can be locked open by means of a plunger if required. Releasing the bolt allows it to go forward and load the first round. On firing, a proportion of the propelling gas is diverted through a port and into a gas cylinder beneath the barrel; this is surrounded by a hollow piston head, so that in effect the piston head is blown off the gas cylinder, driving back the operating rod to actuate the breech by means of the cam. As the bolt goes back, it cocks the hammer, and on the return stroke it collects a fresh cartridge from the box magazine underneath the breech. Magazines for 5, 10, 20 and 30 rounds are available, though this last is only supplied to military and police forces.

Safety catch

The safety catch is in the front of the trigger guard and is simply pushed forward for 'fire' and pulled back for 'safe'. When the last round is fired, the bolt is held open by a catch operated by the magazine follower. The bolt can be closed by means of the bolt release on the left of the receiver or by simply removing the magazine.

In 1977 some minor changes were made to simplify the mechanism and give better protection against dust and dirt, and in 1981 a flash suppressor

Inside the Mini Ruger

The Ruger is a gas-operated, box magazine fed semi-automatic rifle. The rotating bolt is very similar to the M14 and MI Garand from which the Mini is developed, but the gas system of fixed piston and mobile cylinder differs from earlier service rifle designs. Ruger have combined the feel of the M1 carbine with a serious assault rifle calibre to produce an excellent weapon with a very attractive price tag.

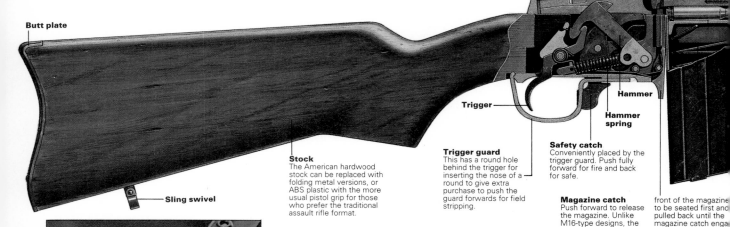

Rearsight
This is adjustable for windage and elevation using the tip of a round. The sight drums are adjustable in ¼ turns, which adjusts the point of impact 1.5 inches when zeroing at 100 m. To raise the mean point of impact, turn the elevation drum anti-clockwise; to move the MPI right turn the windage dial anti-clockwise.

Bolt
The bolt rotates to l the same way as th service rifle.

Firin

Butt plate

Hammer

Hammer spring

Trigger

Stock
The American hardwood stock can be replaced with folding metal versions, or ABS plastic with the more usual pistol grip for those who prefer the traditional assault rifle format.

Trigger guard
This has a round hole behind the trigger for inserting the nose of a round to give extra purchase to push the guard forwards for field stripping.

Safety catch
Conveniently placed by the trigger guard. Push fully forward for fire and back for safe.

Magazine catch
Push forward to release the magazine. Unlike M16-type designs, the

front of the magazine to be seated first and pulled back until the magazine catch enga

Sling swivel

and radioluminous sights were fitted.

The popularity of the Mini-14 with police and security forces led to the development of the Ruger Mini 14/20GB Infantry Rifle. This used the same basic mechanism but had a protected front sight and bayonet lug, grenade launcher fittings on the muzzle, a heat-resistant glassfibre handguard and a flash suppressor.

The Infantry Rifle didn't go as well as might have been expected, largely because most military forces in the late 1970s were looking for weapons with selective fire capability — in other words, they wanted something with

Field stripping the Mini 14

1 Remove the magazine by pressing forward on the release catch located to the rear of the magazine, and pull back on the cocking handle to check that the weapon is clear.

2 Push forward and pivot down the trigger guard to release and remove the trigger assembly as a single unit.

3 Remove the barrel and working parts from the stock by lifting the receiver forwards and upwards.

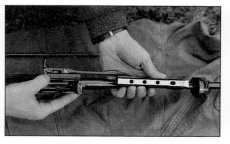

5 Turn the working parts over and remove the recoil spring and guide by pushing it forward to release it and then removing it to the rear. Do not separate the recoil spring from the guide rod. Watch out: the spring is under considerable pressure.

6 Pull the cocking handle connected to the operating rod to the rear, align the locking projections with the cut-outs in the receiver, and remove the whole assembly from the receiver.

7 The recoil spring cup and pin which hold the recoil spring and guide in place will drop out as soon as the tension of the recoil spring is removed. In some models these parts are a permanent fixture and cannot be removed.

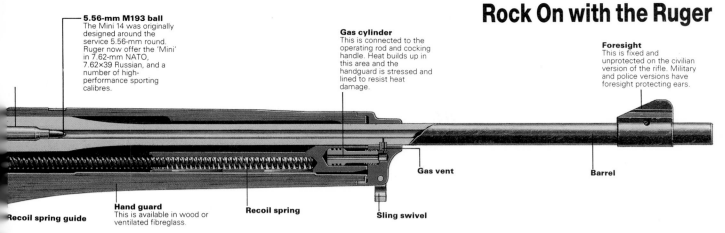

5.56-mm M193 ball
The Mini 14 was originally designed around the service 5.56-mm round. Ruger now offer the 'Mini' in 7.62-mm NATO, 7.62×39 Russian, and a number of high-performance sporting calibres.

Gas cylinder
This is connected to the operating rod and cocking handle. Heat builds up in this area and the handguard is stressed and lined to resist heat damage.

Foresight
This is fixed and unprotected on the civilian version of the rifle. Military and police versions have foresight protecting ears.

Gas vent

Barrel

Recoil spring guide

Hand guard
This is available in wood or ventilated fibreglass.

Recoil spring

Sling swivel

Magazine spring

How the Mini 14 works

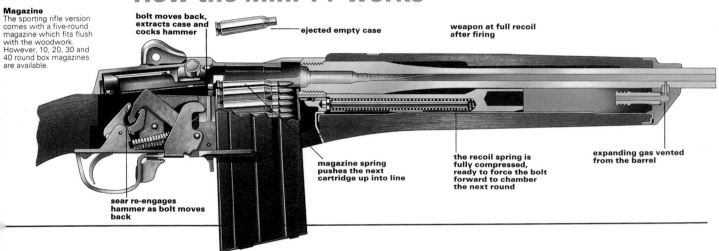

Magazine
The sporting rifle version comes with a five-round magazine which fits flush with the woodwork. However, 10, 20, 30 and 40 round box magazines are available.

bolt moves back, extracts case and cocks hammer

ejected empty case

weapon at full recoil after firing

magazine spring pushes the next cartridge up into line

the recoil spring is fully compressed, ready to force the bolt forward to chamber the next round

expanding gas vented from the barrel

sear re-engages hammer as bolt moves back

4 Remove the plastic resin handguard, which snaps on and off. The handguard also covers the operating handle. The gun is available with wood handguards, which should be left in place.

8 Remove the bolt by pushing it forwards until the front of the bolt lifts out of the receiver, then align the firing pin projection at the back of the bolt within the cut-out in the receiver and remove. This is a little fiddly until you get used to it.

9 The weapon should not be stripped further. Reassembly is in reverse order. When cleaning, pay attention to the gas block under the barrel, which is usually heavily fouled with carbon.

automatic fire. So Ruger produced the AC-556 rifle, which was the Infantry Rifle with the addition of a selector switch to permit full-automatic fire at about 750 rounds per minute. This was followed by the AC-556K, a version with a shorter barrel (330 mm instead of 470 mm) and a pistol grip and folding stock. With the stock folded the overall length of the AC-556K is no more than 603 mm,

The Mini is a surprisingly accurate package, with no recoil to speak of. It can happily compete with some of its more expensive 5.56-mm rifles and will be popular with those who want a rifle that still uses wood rather than plastic.

Battlefield Evaluation: comparing

Ruger Mini-14

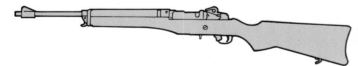

The Ruger Mini-14 is a highly popular weapon in the USA and has achieved extensive sales to police forces worldwide. It is by no means an exact scaling down of the M-14 rifle, since the chamber pressure generated by the 5.56-mm round is actually higher than the 7.62-mm NATO round fired by the larger rifle. A light and handy rifle, the basic Mini-14 is now supplemented by a number of interesting variants. The latest of these is chambered for the standard Soviet 7.62-mm×39 round.

Specification: (self-loading Mini-14)
Cartridge: 5.56-mm×45
Weight: (gun empty) 2.9 kg
Length: 946 mm
Rate of fire: 40 rounds per minute
Magazine: 5-, 20- or 30-round box

Assessment
Reliability	★★★
Accuracy	★★★
Age	★★
Worldwide users	★★★

The basic Mini 14 has been developed into a weapons family, including the compact semi-auto carbine version.

Mini-14/20GB Infantry Rifle

This is the basic Mini-14 adapted for military use, but the idea of a self-loading 5.56-mm weapon went down like a lead balloon. To toughen the rifle for the rigours of service life, the front sight is protected and the handguard is built from heat-resistant fibreglass. A bayonet lug is provided and the barrel sports a flash hider/grenade launcher.

Specification: (Infantry Rifle)
Cartridge: 5.56 mm M193
Weight: (including 20-round magazine) 3.1 kg
Length: 946 mm
Rate of fire: 40 rounds per minute
Magazine: 20- or 30-round box

Assessment
Reliability	★★★
Accuracy	★★★
Age	★
Worldwide users	—

As a military rifle the Mini 14/20 GB has had limited success, but has done extremely well on the civilian market.

ACC-556 Selective Fire Weapon

Similar in appearance to the 20GB, the ACC-556 is able to fire on full auto at a cyclic rate of 750 rounds per minute. The hand guard is made from ventilated glass fibre to prevent overheating. The fire selector is on the right rear of the receiver and gives you the choice of single shot, three-round burst or full auto. Although barrel length remains the same as the Mini-14 (470 mm), the overall size and weight of the weapon are slightly increased. However, the ACC-556K is a cut-down version with folding stock, 603 mm long with stock folded, with a 330 mm barrel.

Specification: (ACC-556)
Cartridge: 5.56-mm M193
Weight: 3.11 kg (with 20-round mag)
Length: 984 mm
Cyclic rate of fire: 750 rounds per minute
Magazine: 20- or 30-round box

Assessment
Reliability	★★★
Accuracy	★★★
Age	★
Worldwide users	★

The ACC 556 selective fire weapon has a selector lever on the right side of the receiver.

whereas the standard stocked AC-556 is 984 mm long.

Back in the commercial market, in 1982 Ruger produced the 'Ranch Rifle'. This was simply the Mini-14 with some small internal improvements and with the addition of integral telescope sight mounts on the receiver. It was also available in some of the smaller high-velocity commercial calibres. And in 1987 came the latest addition to the family, the 'Mini-Thirty'; you might expect that, with a name like that, the rifle would be chambered for the venerable 'thirty-thirty' cartridge, but in fact the truth is more remarkable than that. It is chambered for the Soviet 7.62-mm×39 M43 cartridge, one of the very few rifles of the Western World to be capable of firing the common Soviet army round. It makes a great deal of sense, because the Mini-Thirty is capable of taking the recoil, and with its 470mm barrel, longer than that of the Kalashnikovs, it is capable of delivering better accuracy from the M43 cartridge than any other rifle. It remains to be seen how popular this new addition will be.

Ruger's Ranch rifle version is optimised for use with a scope with built-in scope mounts. Out to 300 metres the Mini will certainly take some beating. Note the method of inserting the magazine.

the Ruger Mini-14 with its rivals

.30 cal M1 carbine

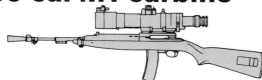

The Mini-14 cashed in on the continuing popularity of the ageing M1 carbine, which the US Army relegated to reserve in 1957 but which remained in demand, particularly from the civilian market. Light and easy to shoot, it fires a low-powered .30-cal round that has little stopping power. However, this makes it safer than many other weapons in urban internal security firefights, and it is used by the Royal Ulster Constabulary. Over five million M1s have been made, and the ammunition is still manufactured.

Specification: (M3 selective fire version)
Cartridge: .30 M1
Weight: 2.36 kg (empty)
Length: 904 mm
Cyclic rate of fire: 750 rounds per minute
Magazine: 15- or 30-round box

Assessment
Reliability	★★★
Accuracy	★★
Age	★★★★★
Worldwide users	★★★

The M1 carbine handles very well, but the stopping power on the .30-cal round leaves something to be desired.

CETME Model L 5.56-mm rifle

As the Mini-14 is a 5.56-mm development of the M1 and M14 7.62-mm rifles, so the CETME Model L is a smaller calibre version of the CETME 7.62-mm rifles. Like the selective fire versions of the Mini-14, the Model L also offers the three-round burst option as well as single shot or full auto on the fire selector. Twenty-round magazines were originally supplied, but the gun now accepts standard US M16 30-round magazines, which may be cheap and nasty but are in service worldwide.

Specification:
Cartridge: 5.56-mm
Weight: 3.6 kg unloaded
Length: 925 mm
Cyclic rate of fire: 700-800 rounds per minute
Magazine: 30-round box

Assessment
Reliability	★★★
Accuracy	★★★
Age	★
Worldwide users	★

The Model L is not up to the quality of HK, but is still a very good gun for the money.

Beretta AR70

The Beretta AR70 uses the forward-locking bolt system used by the M1 Garand, but comparison of the specifications below shows how a conventional 5.56-mm military rifle differs from the Ruger series. The AR70 is lighter than many 5.56-mm weapons but is substantially heavier than the Mini-14. It fires the MECAR 40-mm grenade using a ballistite cartridge and offers single shot or full auto but no burst fire option.

Specification:
Cartridge: 5.56-mm SS109 or M193
Weight: 4.1 kg (with 30-round mag)
Length: 955 mm
Cyclic rate of fire: 650 rounds per minute
Magazine: 30-round box

Assessment
Reliability	★★★
Accuracy	★★★
Age	★★
Worldwide users	★

The Beretta AR70 is a little up-market of the Mini 14, and this is reflected in the price.

Survival Bows

IMPORTANT SAFETY NOTE

Bows can kill! Treat them like a firearm. Never point your bow and arrow at something you do not intend to shoot. When practising, check your backdrop: if you can't see that it is safe to shoot, don't. Never shoot at anything on the skyline.

One surprising omission from most survival training and survival literature (including Special Forces) is a weapon that has been used by millions of men and women, and all young boys, from the stone age to the present — the bow and arrow. This may be because the skills of bow-maker, arrowsmith, fletcher and archer are not perfected overnight, and you don't learn them best in a survival situation.

The bow and arrow have been ignored in survival training because

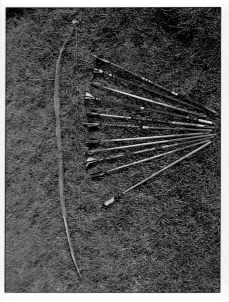

Above: With a little practice you should be able to produce a home-made bow which is a capable hunting weapon. Improvised arrows can be created from a surprising variety of materials and tailored for whatever target you have in mind.

Quiet, lethal and highly accurate in trained hands, the bow is perhaps the finest improvised weapon the survivor can make himself. As with all survival skills, now is the time to learn: don't wait until you need one. Building and shooting a bow requires knowledge and practice but even the complete beginner can soon acquire the necessary skills.

some knowledge of tree types is necessary, and professional bow-makers insist that wood *must* be seasoned for three years to make a bow.

Neither of these notions will hold water. A soldier should be knowledgeable about nature, especially if he is trained in survival techniques. But, yes, a longbow *must* be seasoned for three years – if you want one that will last for years and can drive an arrow-head through the breastplate of a knight at 400 metres. But that's rather unlikely on the modern battlefield.

A deadly weapon

In four lessons, you will be shown how to make a bow in survival conditions. But be warned – when you are cold, hungry, tired and with the "brown adrenalin" flowing, that is not the time to start learning the above skills.

Most survivors or evaders, if offered a weapon that would get their dinner and kill an enemy at a range of up to 150 metres, would say "That'll do nicely, thank you." That weapon can be made in as little as four hours, and

not more than a couple of days depending on materials available, and the power required.

Shooting tips

A strong upper body is both necessary for, and developed by, archery. You need this strength to draw the bow and to hold your aim. In a sur-

A crewmember of a US Navy PBR shoots fire arrows at a hut in the Mekong Delta during the Vietnam war. Commercially built crossbows were used for sentry take-out and assassination in 'spook' operations in South East Asia.

vival situation your strength may be reduced, perhaps greatly, by hunger, fatigue, illness or injury.

ARROW LENGTH

Above: Sizing your arrows is as important as sizing your bow. Measure the correct length as shown here – it is right if the arrow reaches the end of your fingers.

This arrow projects well beyond the fingers so it is really too long. You can still shoot it and an excessively long arrow can be cut down, but an arrow which is too short is dangerous because you could bring it back inside the bow and put it through your hand.

A bracer is essential to protect your forearm from bruising when you release the string. As in all survival situations, making one depends on what you have at hand but if you are planning on several shots, get one organized first.

THE TAB

Above: The tab saves your fingers from being cut by the string. A stout pair of gloves, which every survivor should maintain, will help, but any sustained shooting demands a proper tab.

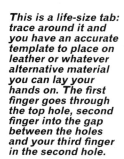

This is a life-size tab: trace around it and you have an accurate template to place on leather or whatever alternative material you can lay your hands on. The first finger goes through the top hole, second finger into the gap between the holes and your third finger in the second hole.

The draw
You pull back the string rather than the arrow, pushing with your left hand while bringing your right hand back. The effort is shared by both arms while your body remains still.

Short bow
The ideal size of your bow depends on your height and the length of your draw but in a survival situation you have to make the best of what is available.

Snap shot!

Survival archery is quite unlike target shooting. You will probably be shooting at fleeting targets, so you must make every effort to close the range first. A snap shot aimed instinctively will be your most likely option and this is what you must practise. So if your potential dinner comes looking for you, rather than the other way round, you'll be prepared.

Headgear
Don't wear any hat with a peak when shooting because it will interfere with your draw. You must be able to draw the string right back to your face.

Hunting arrow
Commercially made hunting arrows have a large broadhead point and large fletchings which are needed to keep the arrow straight. Ordinary sized fletchings would not prevent an arrow with such a head from veering off course. If you are hunting something the size of a boar, your improvised arrows must copy the characteristics of the hunting arrow.

Targets in the trees
For shooting birds, monkeys and other food sources in the South American jungles, the natives use two sorts of arrows. Some specialise in poisoned arrows which can be very nasty against human opposition. This is a bit ambitious for the average survivor so blunt arrows are your best bet. They do enough damage to knock the target to the ground and you won't lose the arrow if you only wing the target.

'The anchor'
Look at the target as you draw, not your bow and arrow. In theory, the string should come back to touch the middle of your chin and the tip of your nose while you stand at right angles to the target. But for a rapid snap shot you won't have time for all the niceties of target shooting.

If so, do not try ambitious shots. Use a shorter "draw length" – the distance the arrow is drawn – and engage your target from as close a range as possible. A quick, instinctive shot is less likely to go wrong because of fatigue.

In fact, this is often the best way to shoot in any case. Field archery is mostly snap shots, perhaps at moving targets, and target archery bears as much resemblance to it as shooting at Disley does to field-firing or combat shooting.

Some archers are always more accurate with an instinctive shot than an aimed shot. Use the style that suits *you* best.

What to wear

Note the dress of the bowman. Do not wear headgear with a peak – a fatigue cap, for example – even when shooting into the sun, as it will foul your draw.

Gloves are one of the most under-emphasised survival items. After a few days of using fires, building or col-

This fox was found, recently killed. The arrow was shot at it from the home-made bow and passed clean through the target. Game-hunting with a bow is illegal in the UK.

lecting, and using sharp or toxic materials, your hands will get rather painful. For the archer, gloves prevent your holding arm being painfully bruised by the string. Pressure on the fingers on your drawing hand can be very painful without gloves, and is distracting in the aim. But you can make a "shooting tab" and a bracer from hide.

If the skirt of your jacket is hanging, or if the sleeves are bulky, remove the jacket, or it will foul the string when you release it, causing loss of speed, range and accuracy.

Big game
Unless you put a powerful hunting arrow in the right place at a cracking velocity, something the size of a boar will either vanish into the undergrowth taking your arrow with it or come and give you a hard time. In the first case, your presence could be betrayed to the enemy and in the second you could be badly hurt. The moral is: choose easy targets if at all possible.

Eye on target
Keep your eye on the target: do not focus on the aiming mark on the bow or the arrow. How much lead you allow on a moving target has so many variables that you will not know until you experiment with your improvised bow.

Making your Bow

The first step on the road to equipping yourself with a bow and some arrows is to find the materials from which you'll make them — which means knowing how to recognize the right wood where it's growing. You may already be familiar with the species of tree and shrub mentioned in this article, of course. If not, the best ways to find out about them are to ask someone who's country-wise to show them to you, or to go to a botanical garden.

Above: The size and power of a home-made bow are largely dictated by the quality of the wood. What is theoretically the best size bow for the individual survivor may not be possible if the wood is a curious shape or badly knotted.

The correct size of a bow

The bow illustrated is by no means perfect but is an excellent survivor's hunting weapon, able to shoot to 200 metres. It is 1.47 m long, which is quite handy for someone of the author's height (1.75 m). A long bow for someone this height would be 1.85 m long. When deciding what length to make your bow, consider the following:

1 The longer the bow is, the better it will resist a given pull.
2 If you change your mind and shorten an existing bow it will shoot further for the same draw but will be harder to pull and is more likely to break.
3 Experiment to find your ideal draw length and try to make your bow to suit, but any bow drawing between 60 and 90 cms will be sufficient for most 'survival archery'.
A bow should not bend in the middle — the central foot or so should be rigid. To determine the position of the handgrip, find the centre of the bow, then mark 75 mm below and 25 mm above. This section will be the handle. The arrow is shot from the bow centre while you grip beneath it. The upper part of the bow should be cut slightly more than the lower in order to compensate for the handle. Trim your bow to its finished size, then cut the nocks at either end.

It is far easier to make your bows and arrows from a straight length of wood. One of the best sources is trees which have been toppled but still have roots in the ground, keeping them alive. Subsequent growth tends to be long, straight branches.

This home-made bow has a draw weight of about 60 lbs, which is substantially less than the wooden bows used in medieval times but will be quite adequate for survival purposes. Remember that your bow will take some 'shooting in': it will be much stiffer for the initial shots. Home-made bows will obviously vary enormously in quality; it is all a matter of experiment. Don't be discouraged if your early efforts are not successful.

Make a day of it

If the idea of visiting a botanical garden seems weird, bear in mind that paragraph 87 of the old Air Ministry publication on jungle survival recommends unit visits for aircrew. Servicemen in survival-oriented units should ask their CO to arrange a day visit, which most parks and gardens anywhere in the world will be happy to set up.

A day's visit will give you all the knowledge you need about trees to find the material for a bow. On top of that, you'll learn to recognize a huge variety of edible, medicinal and otherwise useful plants. If you think it's a waste of a day's training, just think about it – it beats the hell out of square-bashing, or humping a loaded Bergen over 50 km!

Let's assume you've now armed yourself with a fair knowledge of the local flora. So what do you look for?

Wood for the bow

Hard, well-seasoned, springy woods are best for making a bow. Don't even think about making one from softwoods such as pine, fir, new elder shoots, larch, spruce, and so on.

Right: Finishing off a home-made bow is a matter of using whatever is available. Theoretically you can progress from axe to knife and complete the shaping with shards of glass. Keep some Stanley knife blades in your survival kit: they are versatile tools ideal for this kind of work.

Survival

Above: A cross-section of yew. When a bow is drawn the back is stretched and the belly compressed. Yew is unique as the sapwood resists tension and the heartwood resists compression.

You'll only be wasting valuable time and energy.

Look for hardwoods like wych elm, elm, oak, ash, rowan, birch, greenheart, wild rose, hornbeam, dagame, lemonwood, osage orange, juniper and ironwood. Some of these will make a good bow, and some will make a passable one. None will make a bow equal to the king of bow woods, the yew.

Poisonous yew

Yew grows in most of Asia, the Americas and throughout Europe. It's very common in southern England, and you'll see it in churchyards, estates, parks and gardens.

Be careful with the yew. The leaves, berry arils, (an extra covering over the fruit), and sap contain a deadly nerve poison, taxine. Celtic warriors dipped their arrows in the yew sap, just to make sure!

So don't use the leftovers from your bowmaking as skewers or spoons or whatever. You won't come to any harm from handling yew, though, as long as you wash the sap off your hands.

A quick one

You can make an excellent bow very quickly – seasoning the wood in a day, over a fire – from rowan. (This is sometimes called mountain ash, in England).

Ideally, you should take the wood from a slim sapling growing in dense wood. This is because trees growing close together have to "shoot for the sun", and so grow slim and straight with few branches low on the trunk: just what you need for a bow. You don't harm the environment by taking a few of these saplings, since you help

the other trees to spread. And if you cover or dirty the stump, you won't leave any sign of your presence to be spotted from the air.

Sweet rowan

Rowan bows are "sweet" to use, giving no jar or kick. But they do creak ominously when you're shooting them in. It takes fine judgement and a steely nerve to find out how far you can draw them – but then a good bow properly drawn is seven-eighths broken!

Tools of the trade

Once you've selected your bow stave, you'll need some tools to carve the actual bow from it. Professional bowmakers first use a hammer and

Making the string

The English longbowmen of the Middle Ages used bow strings able to take a weight of 140lbs, and these were made from the stalks of the common stinging nettle. Unfortunately this takes a long time to master, so the average survivor must improvise. Silk is ideal for a bow string because it stretches very little, but it is not available in every survival situation. Nylon paracord is a more feasible material. Although it does stretch a little, this can be taken up when bracing the bow and paracord has the bonus of being near rotproof and very strong.

Ideally a wooden bow should be seasoned before use. Professionally made bows are left to dry out for a year or more, but the survivor has to be a bit quicker. Dry it by the fire then shape it by steaming over boiling water.

Reflexing the bow is a matter of brute strength and careful judgement. While a good bow is seven eighths broken when fully drawn, you don't want to snap your nearly completed weapon.

Recurving is achieved by steaming the wood and gently applying pressure. This allows you to mould the wood slowly but surely and without creating any stresses. If you are lucky, you may find a length of wood which is already a good enough shape.

steel wedges to split logs into workable dimensions. Then a small hand-axe trims the stave to the rough shape and size of the bow. A spokeshave brings it down to the exact size, with final minute shavings removed with shards of glass.

In the middle of nowhere and on the run you're not too likely to have any of these. But an issue-type machete or a heavy survival knife will do the job, given some skill and elbow grease.

It's always worth having at least two Stanley knife blades in your survival kit. You can use them on their own as scalpels for fine work, and you can use one to cut its own wooden handle. You can use the Stanley to make your bow from scratch, but it's invaluable for making arrows.

Bracing a bow

Putting the string on a bow is called bracing, and it is very important to get this right. Place your hand 'thumbs up' on the back of the bow: the string should touch your thumb when correctly braced. You need not be too slavish to this rule with a survival bow, but the nearer the better. Use a timber hitch to tie the bottom end of the string permanently in place and use a simple loop to attach it at the top. When you need the bow, brace it and slip on the top loop. Always unstring the bow when not in use or it will lose strength and never leave it standing on end.

Your bow is correctly braced if the string touches the tip of your thumb when you give a 'thumbs up' as shown above.

If you haven't got any of these, tough titty. It's back to basic stone-age survival technology.

Parts of the bow

Bows are described by their shape when they are unstrung, not braced. Note the reflexed bow and the recurved bow are curved away from the belly. Three quarters of the handle is below the centre of the bow and the bow string corresponds to this, so that if the bow string is braced the wrong way round the nocking point for the nock of the arrow will not correspond to the centreline of the bow. Cheap practice bows are available in nylon and fibreglass.

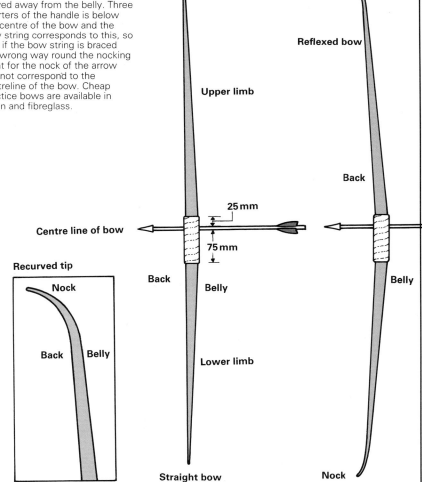

Season the wood

Now to making the bow. Look for a branch or trunk of the right wood that's as straight as possible (there are a few exceptions: see diagrams). It should be at least 6ft 6in long, although you can go as short as 4ft. If you can get a piece of seasoned – that is, properly dried-out – wood, terrific. Look for uprooted trees, cuttings and trimmings, at rail- and roadsides, and near farms and houses.

In conventional bowmaking the entire log is seasoned, sometimes for years, and then thinned down to a bow. Survivors have to reverse the process, and cut out the rough bow and then dry it. This is a lot faster, though it may cause some warping. Trim the stave to the approximate size of the bow, leaving a good quarter inch surplus in both thickness and breadth.

At this point, decide how quickly you need your bow. Some woods you can use straight off, but *all* of them improve enormously with drying out. In a very hot climate a day or two makes a huge difference, and the bow keeps improving as you use it. In cold or temperate climates you will have to dry it over or near your fire. Yew and rowan make the best quick-dried bows.

Straight up

While you have the bow near the fire, you may as well make sure that the stave is straight when viewed from the back or belly.

If you heat – or, preferably, steam – the staff where it's bent, you can put it permanently into shape by applying pressure in the right direction. This doesn't set up any stresses in the wood.

You can also recurve or reflex the bow by the same method. But if the stave you've chosen is naturally re-flexed, or recurved at one end or the other, don't straighten it. If it ain't broke, don't fix it!

Making Your Arrows

'**The Black Rain of Death' — that was how the cloud of arrows descending on the French at Agincourt was described.** Five thousand English archers, with Welsh and Scots mercenaries, each shot 12 arrows per minute into a French force that had been channelled by the terrain into a tightly packed mass in a very small area.

In Vietnam, the Americans mounted banks of motorised machine-guns into "Puff the Magic Dragon", an old Dakota aircraft,to to try to achieve the same effect. The sight of the plunging cloud of arrows was probably psychologically devastating, and even more deadly. The English archers certainly got a better kill ratio than the Americans ever did, and that includes John Wayne in *The Green Berets*!

The arrow is at once both beautifully simple and extremely sophisticated. It is a *missile*, developed by human ingenuity over thousands of years. Many of the lessons learnt in the manufacture of *millions* of these missiles, with hundreds of variations, were forgotten after the Middle Ages,

Arrows must be carefully tailored to the bow which shoots them, so if you make a bow in a survival situation you must tailor your arrows accordingly.

only to be painstakingly re-learnt by 20th-century missile scientists.

Survival is simpler

For survival purposes, you will not have to make an arrow anywhere near as good as those used at Agincourt, which had heavy armour-piercing warheads and had to withstand 120 lbs thrust from the string.

The first thing to learn about arrows is that the missile (the arrow) must

Above: A selection of improvised arrows. Bamboo is one of the most useful materials for making arrows. The dead canes can be used immediately but freshly cut green ones should be allowed to dry out.

match its launcher (the bow). At this stage, an explanation of what's known as the Archer's Paradox is helpful. Due to the impact of the string, the inertia in the arrow, and the fact that the arrow is set at an angle to the string

Making Your Arrows

(which is in line with the centre line of the bow), and the edge of the bow, the arrow actually bends over the bow when you release it. You will not see this with the naked eye, but it does happen. When it leaves the bow, the arrow springs the other way and, after a few more bucks, straightens out and flies off to your target.

If the arrow is too weak for the bow, it will wobble in flight and lose power. It may also break, usually about 6 inches from the nock, usually with jagged edges, and usually getting stopped by the inside of your wrist, which is damned painful. If the arrow is too strong, it will go off a little to your left (if you are right-handed).

For survival purposes, you don't have to match bow and arrow exactly. Instead, learn how each of your arrows flies. It is better in every way to err on the side of the strong arrow.

Woods to use

So now we have the theory, let's make some arrows before we starve to death! Good woods are birch, ash,

The best flights are the feathers of large gliding birds. Whether you use a pelican feather or flamingo's depends on your surroundings. In the UK you'll often have to make do with something off a dead crow.

hornbeam, alder, willow, bamboo, ramin, pine, fir, oak, elm, beech, elder, dog rose, bramble and some reeds. As a survivor you will do best by not confining yourself to the rules, but to use your common sense.

The simplest, quickest, and most versatile wood is bamboo, which is *not* confined to the jungle but is common world-wide. Bamboo breaks always have many dead canes amongst the green; these can be used instantly – dry the green ones near the fire, or leave them for a few days after cutting. Don't forget that you can eat the young shoots, raw or cooked, after you remove the poisonous hairs along the edges of the leaves! Next (for ease, not quality) come strong reeds, followed by willow. Surprisingly, thick bramble and wild rose can provide good arrows. The thorns are easily re-

Left: Step by step construction of a stone arrowhead. This is a long process and a good technique will only come with practice. For survival purposes, a sharpened end will often be your best option and is perfectly adequate at close ranges.

Above: The survivor's arrowheads (left to right): two stone heads gently wedged into the split arrow; a sharpened stick; and lastly, a blunt-headed arrow for hunting birds or small game.

1195

Making the flights

1 Left: The countryside has been littered with plastic cartons and other rubbish. For the survivor this can be very useful: plastic can be cut into flights for your arrows.

2 Above: Slit the cane with two cuts. The first goes right the way through the arrow and the second one, cut at 90 degrees to the first, only goes halfway.

3 Above: Insert the plastic flights and secure the end of the arrow with string/twine or anything you have available. Fire the arrow a few times to assess its flight characteristics; adjust the flights if necessary.

4 Right: The completed arrow rests on a woolly hat with Zippo lighter. Plastic can be moulded to shape with a little gentle heating, but be careful not to let the flame actually ignite it.

moved with your front teeth, leaving a nice round shaft.

The shaft

The arrow should be as straight as you can make it, as bends and kinks cause inaccuracy and wind resistance. Use steam, or bend it over a warm stone, to straighten it, as you did making your bow. Some woods you can straighten cold, either by bending and holding for a minute, or by tying the bow with thread or string and

leaving it for an hour or so.

It is easier than you think to cut an arrow from a billet of wood, especially the softwoods such as pine, using your knife or, better still, your Stanley blade from your survival tin, suitably mounted.

If you have the time, it is back to stone-age technology for a sanding block, to give perfect roundness. Make this from two pieces of sandstone, about 2½ by 1½ by 1 inch. Chip out a semi-circular groove along the

Organising a good set of flights for your arrow is vitally important for accurate shooting. Crow's feathers are good, but if you plan on eating the bird itself make sure it was not poisoned.

Your survival bow is not restricted to hunting on the land. These South American fish arrows are carved so that they stay in a madly wriggling fish after you have shot it. The triple pointed arrow gives you a better chance of a hit and the possibility of multiple penetration.

length of each one. When you put one on top of the other, they should make a circular groove that's the same diameter you want your arrows to finish up. Draw the arrow through these blocks until it's smooth. A far better device, if you can make one, is a small steel plate ⅛ inch thick with a 'V' cut in it. This cuts better, *and*

allows you to vary the diameter of the arrow.

The flights

By far the easiest way to fit the flights is to use plastic – not quite as good as feathers, but requiring much less skill, time and effort. Sadly, there is no shortage of plastic litter anywhere. Near houses, where farmers, climbers, or forestry workers are, along any roadside, beach – in fact, just about anywhere – you will find a profusion of plastic pop bottles, oil cartons, milk cartons, etc.

Cut them into strips with your Stanley blade or knife. If necessary, put them momentarily in boiling water or near heat for a few seconds to soften them, then smooth them flat. Fix them as shown in the photograph.

If you use feathers, those of geese or large gliding birds are best – for example the eagle, buzzard, hawk, flamingo, pelican, crow, seagull or turkey. A good place to find them are farmers' or game keepers' gibbets. You've seen the sort of thing: rows of dead, smelly, decomposing crows hanging upside down on fences to scare other crows away. They'll never notice if you take one! Use the large flight feathers from the wing. Do not mix feathers from right and left wings, if you can help it – it causes wobbling and loss of power, as they set up opposing wind currents.

Positioning the flights

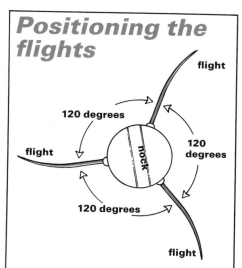

The flights should be positioned at 120 degree intervals. Plastic flights will need a little moulding to give them a slight curve, and if you are using bird feathers do not mix the feathers from either wing: this will make the arrow wobble and reduce its velocity.

Arrowheads and nocks

You can make your arrowheads out of steel, slate, stone, bone, flint, horn, glass, or just sharpened wood. You can even use staples from a fence post.

For the nock, it's simplest just to groove the wood. Put a whipping above the nock to prevent it splitting, if necessary.

The archer's paradox

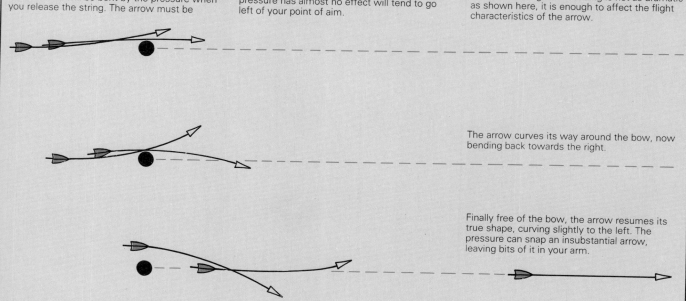

Your arrows must be tailored to your bow in much the same way that a specific calibre bullet will only fit certain rifles. When an arrow is loosed at its target, it begins at a slight angle to the bow and will be bent by the pressure when you release the string. The arrow must be strong enough to cope with the pressure from the bow, otherwise it will be hopelessly inaccurate or even snap. On the other hand, an arrow which is so strong that the bow's pressure has almost no effect will tend to go left of your point of aim.

The bowstring is released and the arrow begins to move. In fact, a slow motion camera would reveal that the arrow bends around the bow to the left. Although the bending is not as dramatic as shown here, it is enough to affect the flight characteristics of the arrow.

The arrow curves its way around the bow, now bending back towards the right.

Finally free of the bow, the arrow resumes its true shape, curving slightly to the left. The pressure can snap an insubstantial arrow, leaving bits of it in your arm.

Fighting Fit

Going for your Stripes

As a section commander you must be able to navigate accurately and at speed. Exercise Cheshire Cat is the first introductory navigation exercise across varying terrain around the Usk reservoir.

A Gurkha studies the map, working out his next leg. On Sennybridge it rapidly becomes obvious that the shortest distance between two points is not a straight line. You will need to look very carefully at contours to avoid ups and downs and 'moon' grass.

Promotion is something that every soldier will consider at some point in his career. Soldiering abilities and leadership potential may be enough to gain you that first stripe, but to become a full corporal you'll have to pass a Non-Commissioned Officer (NCO) Course.

Of Britain's combat troops only the Royal Marines are entirely independent in the way they select NCOs. The Army has the option either to promote from within the Regiment, or to send a man to the School of Infantry (SOI) at Dering Lines, Brecon. The one exception is the Parachute Regiment, where it is mandatory for NCOs to qualify at the SOI. As with the Marines, this ensures that all junior commanders are of the same high calibre.

To be eligible for promotion you should have served in a battalion for at least two years. In addition, you must have been a JNCO for at least a year, and a Section 2iC for nine months or more. You must then convince your unit that you are ready for the course. The ideal candidate is physically and mentally prepared to learn. You must be fit. You need to be enthusiastic, well-motivated and determined. You have to be willing to listen to advice and able to accept criticism. A sense of humour also helps!

Two-phase training

Candidates undergo a total of 12 weeks' training, divided into two phases. The initial six weeks take place at Aldershot and York and cover all aspects of Skill at Arms. Phase Two combines these skills with field work, theory being covered in the classrooms at Dering Lines.

According to the course Sergeant Major, Week One is "a nice, casual,

intimate way to introduce [the candidates] to the way of things. There's nothing too difficult. We don't hit them with anything too hard. It becomes more intensive as the course progresses.''

Teaching, not testing

At Brecon, leadership is taught by example. Many may think – wrongly – that it is a *testing* course. It is not. The OC JNCO Division is emphatic that the SCBC is a *teaching* course. A candidate quickly finds that there's a lot to learn!

The practical field exercises take place mainly on the vast Sennybridge Training Area (SENTA). For many, it is their first-ever glimpse of this inhospitable place. For others, the area brings back happy memories of basic

The course is very much concerned with assimilating vast quantities of information in a limited period. Here an instructor briefs the course for the next phase.

training. SENTA is a large area of rolling hills. Rivers and streams crisscross the countryside and forestry blocks frequently break up an otherwise bleak landscape.

The ground varies, from soft, springy tussocks to waterlogged marshland. Except for the occasional road, tracks are either wet and muddy, or hard-baked and dusty, depending on the season. Apart from those in the forestry blocks, the trees that dot SENTA always seem to lack foliage. They give a forbidding look to an already barren setting. There is little

Above: After the course introduction you are broken down into the sections you will remain in for the course. You will work very closely with these colleagues for the next few weeks, taking turns as section commander on exercises.

Left: The course gives the brains as much of a beating as the body. Lectures are very professionally presented by people who have done the course. There is a lot to learn in very little time.

wildlife here, but SENTA provides ideal grazing for countless sheep. Its very remoteness makes the area such a perfect training ground.

Exercise Cheshire Cat, on Day Three, is a 'basic' day navigation/orienteering exercise. You are each allowed two hours in which to locate nine checkpoints spread over a seven-kilometre course around nearby Usk Reservoir. Points are awarded for each checkpoint found. A total less than 65 means a fail. Sixty six to 75 earns you a 'C' passmark; 76 to 90 a 'B' and anything over 90 an 'A'.

To cover the seven kilometres, you have to run for much of the way. You are laden with kit, and soon begin to feel the strain. Up hill and down; across bog-land and rivers; through forests and along tracks. Checkpoints consist of prominent white and orange markers. Each has a different card punch attached, which is used to

There are things that the section commander must not be without. As an NCO you lead by example and set the standard: no excuses. Daily inspections make sure you are carrying the right kit for the job.

clip the corresponding number on your checkpoint card.

After a tiring two hours most of you arrive at the finish, where you are rewarded with a hot meal and steaming tea. It's certainly appreciated!

Towards nightfall a chill wind begins to blow and the temperature plummets. As soon as it's dark, you're again despatched on 'Point to Point', a night navigation exercise. You don't arrive back at Dering Lines until the early hours of Thursday morning.

NCOs are primarily the teachers of skills in the army. Your job is to pass on skills to your section and then check that they have learned them. One day, these skills may be tested in war. Here course members recce the ground for a battle handling exercise.

As a section commander your personal admin has to be spot on: you will be commanding the section and will not have time to spare. Every man must produce the kit as the instructor reads it off the list, and it is then inspected.

In the classroom

Much of Week One entails spending long periods on theory. A variety of subjects is covered: map reading, battle procedure, admin, in the field, section battle drills, platoon battle drills, attack battle drills, air photography, receipt and delivery of orders, extraction of orders, and more.

Friday sees the first of many visits to SENTA where, weather permitting, you will be shown a demonstration of the 66-mm LAW followed by a section attack. After a 'haybox' lunch, you'll spend the afternoon rehearsing section battle drills.

Saturday is another classroom day and a continuation of the Orders lessons begun two days previously.

Week One also sees the first of several PT tests. With the course company broken down into platoons (each comprising three sections), you will all take your turn at an early morning run.

Yours is the first course to try the revised official army test, running three miles in 33 minutes or under, as opposed to the old two miles in 18 minutes. The weight of equipment carried has also been changed – down from 35lbs to 29lbs. Nevertheless, a number of men find it difficult to keep up. Unlike basic training, there is little encouragement from your instructors, whose attitude indicates that those of you who are physically unfit simply shouldn't be here!

Combat Report
Vietnam:
Pursuing the NVA

Jeremy Thomson was a buck sergeant with a platoon of the 1st Air Calvalry Division in mid-1966 during Operation Masher/White Wing, a 41-day series of battles on the coastal edge of Vietnam's central highlands.

We were crouching under our ponchos in one of those persistent Vietnam drizzles that threw the rain at you in diagonal torrents. Our platoon leader, a boyish lieutenant named Sewell, circulated among us, slipping and sliding in the mud, to explain what was happening.

Last night a patrol from a nearby platoon had taken a frontal assault by NVA regulars. They were nursing wounded and trying to keep hold of their part of the An Lao Valley, where the NVA kept hitting us in small-unit actions, hoping to dislodge us. "We're going to work our way up the valley just ahead," Lieutenant Sewell explained. "We're looking for NVA. If we see them, we fight them."

I had just gotten my third stripe and it was my job to keep our heavy weapons squad in order: D'Amico with the M-60 machine-gun, Smith and Rizzuto with the grenade-launchers, and some other guys including another M-60 gunner. We were a miserable collection of rain-drenched sonofabitches, struggling to keep our gear clean under the ponchos.

NVA might be heading our way

We spent three hours humping up that valley in a kind of zigzag pattern, hoping we'd come upon signs if the North Vietnamese were close. It seemed your gear got heavier in the rain, and I was sweating and gasping and cursing when we took a break to dig into our rations. It frightened me that there were men out in that green-canopied jungle who might try to kill me, but it scared me even more that my buddies might think I couldn't 'hack it'. I shared a cigarette with D'Amico (carefully cupped in our hands) and he told me his worries.

"I worry about getting gut-shot. Or blinded. That's worse than getting killed, to have some part of me broken and unfixable."

In early afternoon the valley had gotten steeper but, mercifully, the rain seemed to be letting up. We all came to a halt while the

Troopers from the 1st Cavalry Division (Airmobile) in action during Operation Masher/White Wing near Bong Son in January 1966.

lieutenant talked furiously with somebody on the radio. The word was passed back: another patrol had stumbled onto some NVA five miles west of us. There had been an inconclusive exchange of gunfire. That patrol was not coming in our direction, but other NVA might be heading our way . . .

"We can't call in an air strike in this soup." Suddenly, M-16 rifles were popping off and I heard the thuck! of Rizzuto firing a round with his M-79 grenade-launcher. I looked downhill to the left and saw several blurred shadows racing between the trees, then the bright red of muzzle flashes. More gunfire came from further behind us. We and the North Vietnamese had been paralleling each other along the same slope, only thirty metres apart, hidden from each other by tree trunks and foliage!

"I need a medic!"

"Everybody down!" I heard one of the other sergeants shout. Our guys were suddenly shooting at NVA in all directions – above, below and behind us.

"I need a medic!" someone cried, and I glimpsed Hennesy, the red cross crudely stitched on his helmet cover, crashing through the wet brush.

Now I could feel my heart pounding in my throat. I was responsible for eight men! I think the fear of failing was so strong that I had no time for fear of dying.

"Collins!" I shouted to the other M-60 gunner. "Get over there on that flat, where you can look straight down at 'em! D'Amico, Rizzuto! Work into position to get the NVA on the right."

"They weren't ready for us," Smith said, as if he could read the NVA's minds. The occasional grenade came spiralling down to explode with a soggy thwunk!, but it was clear Smith was right. The NVA hadn't gotten close enough and their rounds were having little effect because the ground was like a sponge.

"Shoot low!" I shouted to one of my guys. It always caused the enemy more trouble if you could wound his men rather than kill them. I crouched over my own M-16 rifle, squeezed off a few rounds, and kept wishing the enemy could be more clearly defined.

"Oh, ****!" I heard the medic crying as he bent over a man from another squad. "Shoulder and neck wound. A lot of arteries broken . . ."

"D'Amico!" I was surprised by the authority in my own voice. "Up higher and further back. That's the way, that's the way . . ."

Co-ordinated fire

In my mind, there was a certain order to the way we were fanning out on the wet slope and responding to the NVA fire. "I got the sonofabitch!" I heard Rizzuto yell. But it must have looked like some madman had grabbed us up and flung us all over that slick, green-brown hillside.

Our initial reaction had prevented the NVA from getting as close as they wanted and now we were laying down co-ordinated fire, but it wouldn't have looked that way to an observer. Americans in muddy uniforms were splayed all over the place, some of them in the open, one man lying in a huge puddle, most partly submerged in wet grass and leafy shrubs.

After several minutes, only our weapons were firing. "Cease fire!" somebody at the front of the column was yelling, and no-one was listening. "Cease fire!" I chimed in. Slowly, we did.

We scrambled down to the creek bed in the

An M-60 gunner from 1st Cavalry near Bong Son. In a series of firefights over several weeks the Allied forces inflicted over 2,000 casualties, but it was rare for a patrol to return with prisoners.

centre of the valley, worked northward a short distance, and came right into the middle of an encampment where the NVA had been bivouacked. The few stragglers who hadn't broken camp were caught on open ground. It was the closest, starkest view I ever had of North Vietnamese soldiers. They were short, dark-featured men and one of them had his trousers down – he had apparently been attending to a call of nature.

Hands went up

I think we all understood what had happened. The NVA we'd fought with had been out on patrol looking for us. After giving up on finding us, they'd blundered into our patrol by mistake, somewhat unprepared. We'd left a couple of NVA dead on that slope back there – my M-60 gunner, D'Amico, really did get one of them – and the rest had bugged out without returning to this camp.

The NVA in front of us began scrambling for their weapons. One of them had an AK-47 in his hand just as one of our guys stitched a pattern of M-16 slugs in the mud around him. There was a sudden pause, hands went up, and our platoon had done the impossible – captured three North Vietnamese prisoners.

On our way back, after the rain cleared long enough for us to locate an LZ and get our wounded man out on a Dustoff helicopter, it started raining again and we came in from patrol tuckered under those ponchos. The lieutenant sought me out. "Not a bad job, sergeant. Your guys were pretty alert."

The fire fight had been brief and, in my mind, inconclusive, but at least I hadn't let my fears win. It was good to know that you could be as scared as I was and still do the right thing.

Fighting Fit

SECTION COMMANDERS BATTLE COURSE: WEEK 2

Battle Preparation

A Gurkha NCO conducts the teaching phase of the battle lesson. Public speaking does not come easily to most people but is one thing you will enjoy as your instructional technique matures.

During the course you will have to satisfy your instructors of your ability to conduct a Battle Lesson (BL). On Monday morning of Week Two, the first BL is taken by a young Gurkha NCO who will have 45 minutes to cover the lesson's four phases:

1 Preliminaries
2 Teaching Phase
3 Exercise Phase
4 Final Administration

You arrive at SENTA, where the NCO is allowed time to prepare the lesson – in this instance, Battle Preparation. Several of you are detailed off as a 'demo party', with one man to act as 'enemy'. The remainder will form the class.

For a change, it isn't raining. It makes things easier for the Gurkha, who selects a pleasant spot alongside a trickling stream. He quickly sets up a visual aids board and sorts out blank ammunition and equipment required for the lesson. As soon as he is ready he calls forward and lines up the demonstration team.

"For inspection, port arms!"

As a standard safety measure, weapons and pouch contents are checked prior to each BL and the distribution of blank rounds. The demo party is given a briefing and ordered to take up positions on a wooded slope just beyond the stream. The class is then called forward and, like the demo party, subjected to a safety check. The Gurkha also asks a few questions about weapons' safety before issuing everyone with blank ammunition. The preliminaries over, you are formed up in front of the aids board for the teaching phase.

The main points of battle preparation are best remembered by the mnemonic PAWPERSO: **P**rotection, **A**mmunition, **W**eapons, **P**ersonal camouflage, **E**quipment, **R**adio, **S**pecial equipment, **O**rders.

Points to remember

Each sub-heading is explained in detail by the Gurkha who, although visibly nervous to begin with, soon gains confidence as the lesson progresses. He concludes the theory side with the obligatory, "Are there any questions on battle preparation?"

There are none, so the course instructor puts a few to the class to make sure that the lesson has sunk in. The eight main points are then covered again, this time during a practical lesson with the assistance of two of the demo team.

By the time the teaching phase is over, you are well prepared for the exercise. This takes place on the nearby hillside and ends in a simple advance-to-contact. Weapons are then unloaded and cleared, and you are all debriefed.

Your section instructor now re-

Preparation for battle includes camming up in pairs. Have a good look at the ground you are going to be moving over before you start. Remember, you will be the model for your section if you are successful, so now is the time to perfect your technique.

sumes command and provides his own detailed debrief. He is careful not to belittle the Gurkha, and is quick to point out the positive aspects of his teaching methods as well as any mistakes. It's a noticeable difference to basic training, where it seemed that only the flaws were ever noticed!

Exercise Rapid Fire is scheduled for immediately after the battle lesson. One of you is nominated as section

Instruction over, the section move off to put theory into practice. The real job satisfaction comes where you pass on your skills to the section and then test and monitor the results. The stream is a good approach route as it provides cover from fire if you come under contact and some cover from view as you move up.

The section commander is at the very sharp end of the infantry battle. Your leadership and skills will largely determine success or failure in the attack.

With live rounds impacting to your front, the gunner opens up with the LSW. Winning the fire fight is of primary importance and tended to be overlooked on training exercises prior to the Falklands war.

The live firing exercise continues, with the command appointments changing as each objective is taken out. The enemy is well dug in: as you clear one trench you fire on the next target in depth.

commander and held responsible for issuing ammunition and preparing for your first live fire exercise.

For the exercise, your section is detailed to take out three bunkers situated at intervals along a wide valley. The weather is unusually mild, but there are drainage ditches that cut across the valley holding several inches of muddy rainwater. With a knee-deep, fast-flowing river winding its way along one side of the range, it looks like you're going to end up soaking wet!

Rapid Fire begins with the section being led across open ground towards the first objective. Armed with a 7.62-mm SLR, the platoon commander follows close behind the lead scouts. Suddenly he raises his rifle and sends a burst into the ground in front of the section! Mud and tufts of grass are hurled high into the air.

"TAKE COVER!"

You instantly respond to the command, running forward a few steps before throwing yourself to the ground. There are shouts of command as your section commander assumes control of the 'battle'. Shots ring out as the target is engaged. You close on the first objective, leap-frogging forward by fire and manoeuvre – a tactic you will have learned years before during recruit training. Then, you simply did as you were told. Now, one of *you* is giving the orders. When you take the second objective it might very well be you who leads the attack! Concentrate!

You find yourself taking cover in a muddy ditch. You peer over the top. Where the hell is the bunker? Remember what you've been taught. If you can't see the target, change your fire position. You might bluff your way by firing into empty space during training – but not for real! Change position. . .there, that's better. The low-lying bunker wavers in the weapon's SUSAT optical sight. Okay, calm down. Breathe in deeply . . . exhale . . . steady, and FIRE! Double tap. Good! Down, shift position slightly to confuse the enemy. Pop up in another spot, come back on aim, and squeeze the trigger.

Fire and manoeuvre. Provide covering fire while another fire team moves forward. Then it's your turn to go. Carry on until a grenade man can get close enough to 'post' his deadly projectile through the bunker's weapon slit. Then reorganise on the shattered bunker.

"STOP!"

The SI suddenly brings you back to reality. The war is held up while he briefs you on each step of the attack. What a hell of a change to the battle lesson you were enjoying – was it really only half an hour ago?

The new section commander issues quick battle orders before fire-and-manoeuvring the section forward to the next position.

The section commander must be fitter than the rest of the section so he can still think when the rest are on their chinstraps. Leadership at this level is concerned with physical courage and 110 per cent effort.